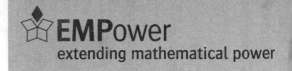

D1003627

Over, Around, and Within
Geometry and Measurement

TEACHER BOOK

TERC

Mary Jane Schmitt, Myriam Steinback,
Tricia Donovan, and Martha Merson

Key Curriculum Press
Innovators in Mathematics Education

TERC, Technical Education Research Centers, Inc.
2067 Massachusetts Avenue
Cambridge, Massachusetts 02140

T E R C

Key College Publishing and Key Curriculum Press:
Development Editor: Elizabeth McCue
Production Director: McKinley Williams
Production Project Manager: Ken Wischmeyer
Consultant: Donna Curry
Text Designer: Laura Murray Productions
Proofreader: Erin Milnes
Photo Researcher: Laura Murray Productions
Art and Design Coordinator: Jensen Barnes
Cover and Logo Design: Kavitha Becker, Marilyn Perry
Cover Photo Credit: CREATAS/Corbis

Editorial Director: Richard J. Bonacci
Vice President/General Manager: Mike Simpson
Publisher: Steven Rasmussen

EMPower Research and Development Team
Principal Investigator: Myriam Steinback
Co-Principal Investigator: Mary Jane Schmitt
Research Associate: Martha Merson
Curriculum Developer: Tricia Donovan

Contributing Authors
Donna Curry
Marlene Kliman

Technical Team
Graphic Designer and Project Assistant: Juania Ashley
Production and Design Coordinator: Valerie Martin
Copyeditor: Jill Pellarin

Evaluation Team
Brett Consulting Group:
  Belle Brett
  Marilyn Matzko

EMPower™ was developed at TERC in Cambridge, Massachusetts. This material is based upon work supported by the National Science Foundation under award number ESI-9911410. Any opinions, findings, and conclusions or recommendations expressed in this publication are those of the authors and do not necessarily reflect the views of the National Science Foundation.

TERC is a not-for-profit education research and development organization dedicated to improving mathematics, science, and technology teaching and learning.

All other registered trademarks and trademarks in this book are the property of their respective holders.

Key Curriculum Press
1150 65th Street
Emeryville, CA 94608
510-595-7000
editorial@keycollege.com
www.keypress.com

Printed in the United States of America
10 9 8 7 6 5 4 3 2   08 07 06

ISBN 1-55953-725-6

EMPower Teacher Participants

Arizona

Gila River Indian Community 21st Century
    Community Learning Center, Gila River
Andrea Parrella

Illinois

Adult Education Center, Rock Valley College,
    Rockford
Phyllis Flanagan, Melinda Harrison

Comprehensive Community Solutions, Inc.,
    YouthBuild, Rockford
Ryan Boyce

Township High School District 214
    Community Education, Arlington Heights
Kathy Conrad

Massachusetts

Action for Boston Community Development, Inc.,
    LearningWorks, Boston
Kelly Qualman

Adult Learning Center at Middlesex Community
    College, Bedford
Roberta Froelich

Brockton Adult Learning Center, Brockton
Marilyn Moses

Community Learning Center, Cambridge
Nellie Dedmon, Sylvia Lotspeich Greene,
    Linda Huntington

Dimock Commuity Health Center, Roxbury
Martha Gray

Harvard Bridge to Learning and Literacy,
    Cambridge
Judy Hikes, Carol Kolenik

Holyoke Adult Learning Opportunities (HALO)
    Center, Holyoke
Kelly Martin, Glenn Yarnell

Hyde Square Task Force, Jamaica Plain
Nora O'Connor

Jewish Vocational Services, Boston
Susan Arase, Terry Lerner, Jeff Snyder

Lowell Adult Education Program, Lowell
Barbara Goodridge

Mount Wachusett Community College, Gardner
Patricia Vorfeld

Notre Dame Education Center, South Boston
Esther D. Leonelli

Pioneer Valley Adult Education Center,
    Northampton
Olu Odusina

Project Place, Boston
Sharon Carey, Maia Hendrickson

Quinsigamond Community College Adult Basic
    Education Program, Worcester
Cathy Coleman

Read/Write/Now, Springfield
Lee E. Boone, Susanne Campagna, Michelle Faith
    Brown, Lucille Fandel

Somerville Center for Adult Learning Experiences
    (SCALE), Somerville
Tom Glannon

X-Cel Adult Education, Dorchester
Don Sands

Maine

Bailey Evening School, Bath
Pam Bessey

Gardiner Adult and Community Education Program
Diann Bailey

Windham Adult Education, Windham
Eva Giles

New Jersey

New Brunswick Public Schools—Adult Learning Center, New Brunswick
Jacqueline Arkoe, Phyllis Boulanger, Sue Helfand, Karen C. Pickering

New York

Adult Learning Center, La Guardia Community College, Long Island City
Norma Andrade, Mark Trushkowsky

BEGIN Managed Programs, New York
Charles Brover, Solange Farina, Santiago Perez, Elizabeth Reddin

Borough of Manhattan Community College/CUNY Adult Basic Education Program, Center for Continuing Education and Workforce Development, New York
Elliot Fink, Mark Lance

City University of New York, Continuing Education, New York
Lisa Simon

Lehman Adult Learning Center, Bronx
Deidre Freeman

SafeSpace-LifeSkills, New York
Jonna Rao

The Adult Learning Center, College of Staten Island, Staten Island
Karen Johnsen

Pennsylvania

Lancaster-Lebanon Intermediate Unit 13/Career Link, Lancaster
Margaret Giordano, Barbara Tyndall

Rhode Island

Dorcas Place, Parent Literacy Center, Providence
Shannon Dolan, Jerelyn Thomas

Tennessee

Hawkins County Adult Education Program, Rogersville
Lisa Mullins

Acknowledgments

Many friends and family members supported the teachers' and EMPower's efforts. Thank you Denise Deagan, Judith Diamond, Cara Dimattia, Ellen McDevitt, Sandy Strunk, and the board of the Adult Numeracy Network. Roberta Froelich, Brad Hamilton, Michael Hanish, David Hayes, Judy Hikes, Alisa Izumi, Esther D. Leonelli, Myra Love, Lambrina Mileva, Luz Rivas, Johanna Schmitt, Rachael Stark, Jonathan Steinback, and Sean Sutherland all made unique and timely contributions to the project.

We appreciate the encouragement and advice from John (Spud) Bradley, EMPower's program officer, and Gerhard Salinger of the National Science Foundation.

We are indebted to every adult student who participated in the piloting of EMPower. Their honest feedback and suggestions for what worked and what did not work were invaluable. We could not have completed the curriculum without them or their teachers.

Contents

Introduction to the EMPower Curriculum

Background

Extending Mathematical Power (EMPower) integrates recent mathematics education reform into the field of education for adults and out-of-school youth. EMPower was designed especially for those students who return for a second chance at education by enrolling in remedial and adult basic education programs, high school equivalency programs, and developmental programs at community colleges. However, the curriculum is appropriate for a variety of other settings as well, such as high schools, workplaces, and parent and paraprofessional education programs. EMPower builds interest and competency in mathematical problem solving and communication.

Over the course of four years (2000–2004), a collaboration of teachers and researchers with expertise in adult numeracy education and K–12 mathematics reform developed and piloted eight contextualized curriculum units. These units are organized around four central topics: number and operation sense; patterns, functions, and relations; geometry and measurement; and data and graphs. The EMPower program serves as a model for a cohesive mathematics curriculum that offers content consistent with the *Principles and Standards for School Mathematics* (NCTM, 2000), as well as frameworks that are adult-focused, such as the *Equipped for the Future Content Standards* (Stein, 2000), the *Massachusetts ABE Curriculum Frameworks for Mathematics and Numeracy* (Massachusetts Department of Education, 2001), and the Adult Numeracy Network's *Framework for Adult Numeracy Standards* (Curry, Schmitt, & Waldron, 1996). The curriculum fosters a pedagogy of learning for understanding; it embeds teacher support and is transformative, yet realistic, for multi-level classrooms.

EMPower challenges students and teachers to consistently extend their ideas of what it means to do math. The curriculum focuses on mathematical reasoning, communication, and problem solving with a variety of approaches and strategies, not just rote memorization and symbol manipulation. The program fosters a learning community in which students are encouraged to expand their understanding of mathematics through open-ended investigations, working collaboratively, sharing ideas, and discovering multiple ways for solving problems. The goal of EMPower is to help people build experience managing the mathematical demands of various life situations, such as finances and commerce, interpretation of news stories, and leisure activities, and to connect those experiences to mathematical principles.

A Focus on Mathematical Content

The EMPower curriculum supports students' and teachers' growth by directing attention to significant mathematical understandings.

EMPower emphasizes:

- Data analysis, geometry and measurement, algebra, and numbers and operations at all student levels.

- Reliance on benchmark numbers—such as powers and multiples of 10, common fractions, and their decimal and percent equivalents—for making mental calculations.

- Early use of calculators to support computation.

- Development of reasoning on proportion and parts of quantities before consideration of formal operations with rational numbers.

- Making decisions about data where students generate, as well as interpret, graphical representations.

- Geometry and measurement based on opportunities to see and touch in developing an understanding of spatial relationships and formulas.

- Leading with patterns and relationships in contextual situations and the representations of these situations with diagrams, tables, graphs, verbal rules, and symbolic notation to develop algebraic competence.

A Focus on Pedagogy

Mathematics is meaningful within a social context. While mathematical truths are universal, the meaning and relevance of numbers changes according to the setting and culture. Therefore, the EMPower pedagogy is focused on sets of connected activities that require communication and discourse.

EMPower asks students to

- Work collaboratively with others on open-ended investigations;

- Share strategies orally and in writing; and

- Justify answers in multiple ways.

Key features of curriculum activities provide

- Clear mathematical goals;

- Contexts that are engaging and useful for young people and adults;

- Opportunities to strengthen mathematical language and communication skills;

- Various ways of entering and solving problems; and

- Puzzles that draw students into problems and motivate them to seek a solution.

Overview of EMPower Units
Features of the Teacher Book

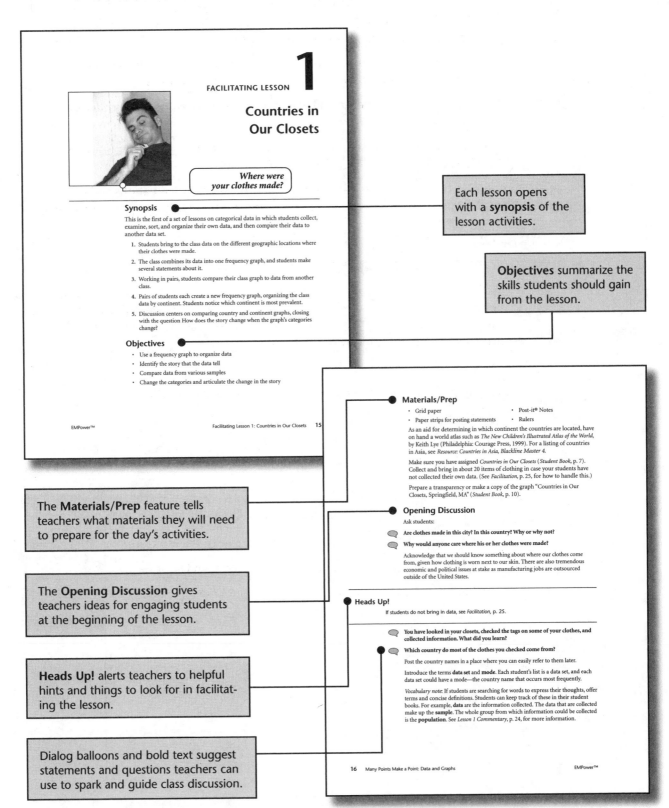

FACILITATING LESSON 1

Countries in Our Closets

Where were your clothes made?

Synopsis

This is the first of a set of lessons on categorical data in which students collect, examine, sort, and organize their own data, and then compare their data to another data set.

1. Students bring to the class data on the different geographic locations where their clothes were made.
2. The class combines its data into one frequency graph, and students make several statements about it.
3. Working in pairs, students compare their class graph to data from another class.
4. Pairs of students each create a new frequency graph, organizing the class data by continent. Students notice which continent is most prevalent.
5. Discussion centers on comparing country and continent graphs, closing with the question How does the story change when the graph's categories change?

Objectives

- Use a frequency graph to organize data
- Identify the story that the data tell
- Compare data from various samples
- Change the categories and articulate the change in the story

EMPower™   Facilitating Lesson 1: Countries in Our Closets   15

Each lesson opens with a synopsis of the lesson activities.

Objectives summarize the skills students should gain from the lesson.

Materials/Prep

- Grid paper
- Paper strips for posting statements
- Post-it® Notes
- Rulers

As an aid for determining in which continent the countries are located, have on hand a world atlas such as *The New Children's Illustrated Atlas of the World*, by Keith Lye (Philadelphia: Courage Press, 1999). For a listing of countries in Asia, see *Resource: Countries in Asia, Blackline Master 4*.

Make sure you have assigned *Countries in Our Closets* (*Student Book*, p. 7). Collect and bring in about 20 items of clothing in case your students have not collected their own data. (See *Facilitation*, p. 25, for how to handle this.)

Prepare a transparency or make a copy of the graph "Countries in Our Closets, Springfield, MA" (*Student Book*, p. 10).

Opening Discussion

Ask students:

💬 **Are clothes made in this city? In this country? Why or why not?**

💬 **Why would anyone care where his or her clothes were made?**

Acknowledge that we should know something about where our clothes come from, given how clothing is worn next to our skin. There are also tremendous economic and political issues at stake as manufacturing jobs are outsourced outside of the United States.

Heads Up!

If students do not bring in data, see *Facilitation*, p. 25.

💬 **You have looked in your closets, checked the tags on some of your clothes, and collected information. What did you learn?**

💬 **Which country do most of the clothes you checked come from?**

Post the country names in a place where you can easily refer to them later.

Introduce the terms **data set** and **mode**. Each student's list is a data set, and each data set could have a mode—the country name that occurs most frequently.

Vocabulary note: If students are searching for words to express their thoughts, offer terms and concise definitions. Students can keep track of these in their student books. For example, **data** are the information collected. The data that are collected make up the **sample**. The whole group from which information could be collected is the **population**. See *Lesson 1 Commentary*, p. 24, for more information.

16   Many Points Make a Point: Data and Graphs   EMPower™

The Materials/Prep feature tells teachers what materials they will need to prepare for the day's activities.

The Opening Discussion gives teachers ideas for engaging students at the beginning of the lesson.

Heads Up! alerts teachers to helpful hints and things to look for in facilitating the lesson.

Dialog balloons and bold text suggest statements and questions teachers can use to spark and guide class discussion.

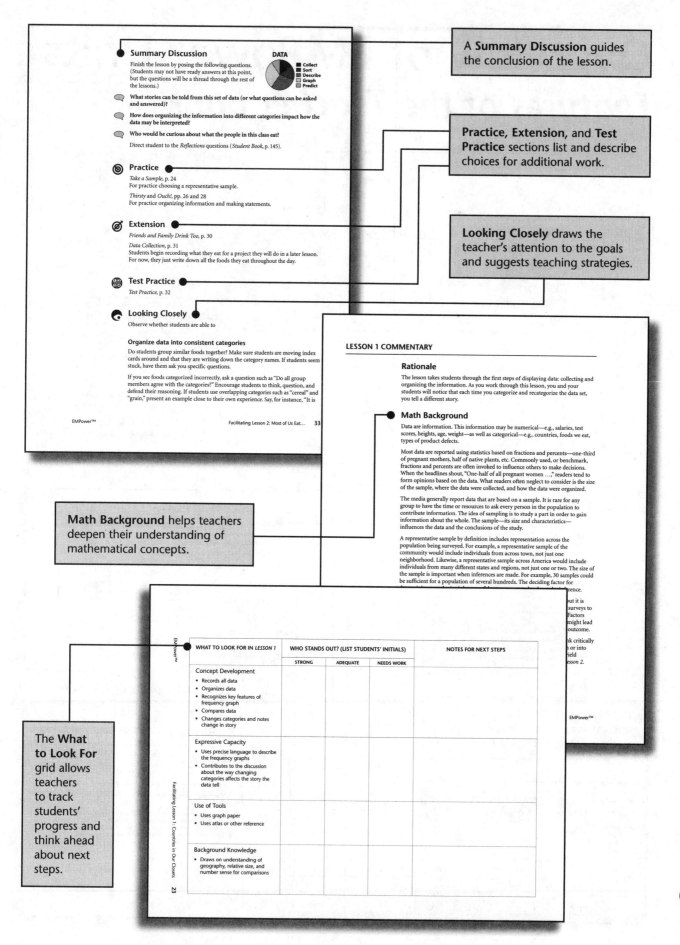

Summary Discussion

Finish the lesson by posing the following questions. (Students may not have ready answers at this point, but the questions will be a thread through the rest of the lessons.)

DATA
- Collect
- Sort
- Describe
- Graph
- Predict

💬 What stories can be told from this set of data (or what questions can be asked and answered)?

💬 How does organizing the information into different categories impact how the data may be interpreted?

💬 Who would be curious about what the people in this class eat?

Direct student to the *Reflections* questions (*Student Book*, p. 145).

◎ **Practice**

Take a Sample, p. 24
For practice choosing a representative sample.

Thirsty and *Ouch!*, pp. 26 and 28
For practice organizing information and making statements.

◎ **Extension**

Friends and Family Drink Too, p. 30

Data Collection, p. 31
Students begin recording what they eat for a project they will do in a later lesson. For now, they just write down all the foods they eat throughout the day.

◎ **Test Practice**

Test Practice, p. 32

◎ **Looking Closely**

Observe whether students are able to

Organize data into consistent categories

Do students group similar foods together? Make sure students are moving index cards around and that they are writing down the category names. If students seem stuck, have them ask you specific questions.

If you see foods categorized incorrectly, ask a question such as "Do all group members agree with the categories?" Encourage students to think, question, and defend their reasoning. If students use overlapping categories such as "cereal" and "grain," present an example close to their own experience. Say, for instance, "It is

EMPower™   Facilitating Lesson 2: Most of Us Eat... **33**

LESSON 1 COMMENTARY

Rationale

The lesson takes students through the first steps of displaying data: collecting and organizing the information. As you work through this lesson, you and your students will notice that each time you categorize and recategorize the data set, you tell a different story.

◉ **Math Background**

Data are information. This information may be numerical—e.g., salaries, test scores, heights, age, weight—as well as categorical—e.g., countries, foods we eat, types of product defects.

Most data are reported using statistics based on fractions and percents—one-third of pregnant mothers, half of native plants, etc. Commonly used, or benchmark, fractions and percents are often invoked to influence others to make decisions. When the headlines shout, "One-half of all pregnant women …," readers tend to form opinions based on the data. What readers often neglect to consider is the size of the sample, where the data were collected, and how the data were organized.

The media generally report data that are based on a sample. It is rare for any group to have the time or resources to ask every person in the population to contribute information. The idea of sampling is to study a part in order to gain information about the whole. The sample—its size and characteristics—influences the data and the conclusions of the study.

A representative sample by definition includes representation across the population being surveyed. For example, a representative sample of the community would include individuals from across town, not just one neighborhood. Likewise, a representative sample across America would include individuals from many different states and regions, not just one or two. The size of the sample is important when inferences are made. For example, 30 samples could be sufficient for a population of several hundreds. The deciding factor for ... ...rence.

...but it is ...surveys to ...Factors ...might lead ...outcome.

...nk critically ...h or into ...field ...*esson 2.*

EMPower™

WHAT TO LOOK FOR IN *LESSON 1*	WHO STANDS OUT? (LIST STUDENTS' INITIALS)			NOTES FOR NEXT STEPS
	STRONG	ADEQUATE	NEEDS WORK	
Concept Development • Records all data • Organizes data • Recognizes key features of frequency graph • Compares data • Changes categories and notes change in story				
Expressive Capacity • Uses precise language to describe the frequency graphs • Contributes to the discussion about the way changing categories affects the story the data tell				
Use of Tools • Uses graph paper • Uses atlas or other reference				
Background Knowledge • Draws on understanding of geography, relative size, and number sense for comparisons				

EMPower™

Facilitating Lesson 1: Countries in Our Closets **23**

A Summary Discussion guides the conclusion of the lesson.

Practice, Extension, and **Test Practice** sections list and describe choices for additional work.

Looking Closely draws the teacher's attention to the goals and suggests teaching strategies.

Math Background helps teachers deepen their understanding of mathematical concepts.

The **What to Look For** grid allows teachers to track students' progress and think ahead about next steps.

Context

Some students may know about *maquiladoras* in Mexican border towns, where women make clothes for very little money and with no benefits or environmental Occupational Safety and Health Administration (OSHA) workplace protections. CorpWatch (www.corpwatch.org) is one source for information on *maquiladoras*.

Facilitation

If students do not bring in data, or if their sample is too small, skip the second part of the *Opening Discussion*. Have available a pile of 20 clothing articles with labels. First, ask students to predict where the clothes were made. Post the list of their guesses. Note that it will be hard for them to answer this question unless they organize the information on the labels. Then divide up the 20 articles of clothing. Have students write the name of the country for each piece of clothing on a Post-it Note, one country name per note. Ask: "Where are most of our clothes made?" Then continue with the activity.

Making the Lesson Easier

Frequency graphs lend themselves to comparisons among categories. If students have little fluency stating comparisons, you may choose only to compare size, using terms like "greater," "fewest," or "less than." For students who are encountering data formally for the first time, the notion that collapsing data yields different stories may be difficult. Treat this lightly in the activity, and revisit such questions after students have more experience categorizing and recategorizing data in the homework and in *Lesson 2*.

Making the Lesson Harder

If your students can handle benchmark fractions and percents, get them to look critically at the data, including the source and sample size. You might ask:

> If we asked another class what countries are in their closets, what do you think would happen to the categories? What if we asked the entire community?

> How do you think your data would compare to data from another class of adult students in another community?

If students struggle with the idea of sample, you might try this: Have them each write their favorite color on a Post-it Note. If you have a small class, ask them to write the color on two Post-it Notes. Place all of the notes in a container. Have someone randomly (eyes closed) choose a few notes from the container and place them across a line to form a frequency graph. Ask the students how they think this sample compares to the actual total number of colors on notes in the container. You can have them do another frequency graph to compare the sample to the actual total.

The authors give ideas for Making the Lesson Easier and Making the Lesson Harder.

LESSON 1 IN ACTION

Alice articulates the mathematical principle behind compressed data.

> I asked, "How did the change in categories affect what we noticed about the data?"
>
> Alice answered, "Well, we keep losing information."
>
> "How so?"
>
> Patiently, Alice explained that when we started our work, every bit of data was visible. She added that we had lost details initially recorded. "At first, we knew every country in every person's closet and how many pieces of clothing came from that country. Then we combined the data, and we lost track of who had which countries. Then we did it by continent, and we lost track of all the countries."
>
> Alice's realization quickly gained agreement from the rest of the class. After all, just the previous week a classmate had noted, "When you change the amount of data you look at, you find different things."
>
> Sonia added her comment with increased conviction: "It is like politics. Politicians use a graph and tell you this is true, but you look at the graph, and it does not tell you everything."
>
> *Tricia Donovan*
> *Pioneer Valley Adult Education Center, Northampton, MA*

In Lesson in Action, EMPower teachers share their classroom experiences.

Overview of EMPower Units
Features of the Student Book

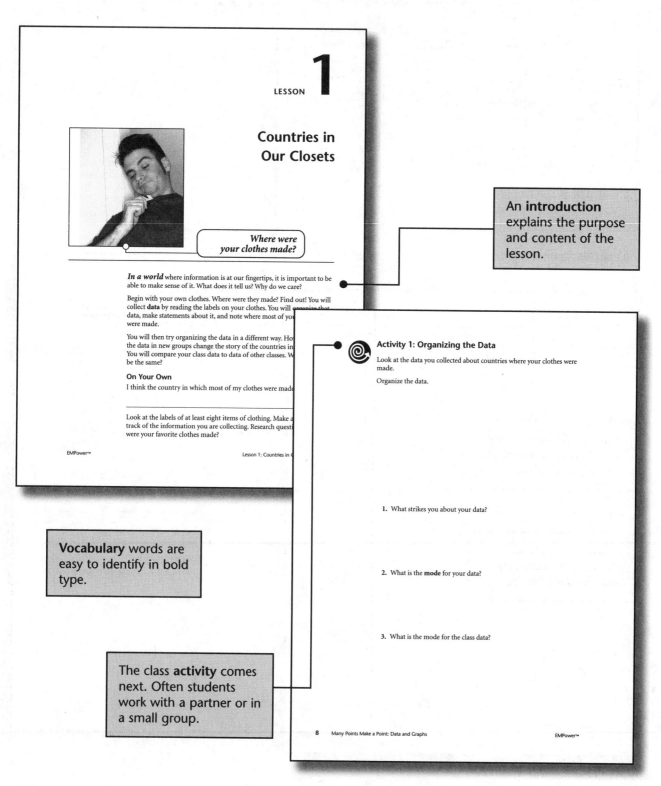

LESSON 1

Countries in Our Closets

Where were your clothes made?

In a world where information is at our fingertips, it is important to be able to make sense of it. What does it tell us? Why do we care?

Begin with your own clothes. Where were they made? Find out! You will collect **data** by reading the labels on your clothes. You will organize that data, make statements about it, and note where most of you~~r clothes~~ were made.

You will then try organizing the data in a different way. Ho~~w~~ the data in new groups change the story of the countries in ~~...~~ You will compare your class data to data of other classes. W~~...~~ be the same?

On Your Own

I think the country in which most of my clothes were made ~~...~~

Look at the labels of at least eight items of clothing. Make a ~~...~~ track of the information you are collecting. Research questi~~...~~ were your favorite clothes made?

EMPower™   Lesson 1: Countries in ~~...~~

An **introduction** explains the purpose and content of the lesson.

🌀 **Activity 1: Organizing the Data**

Look at the data you collected about countries where your clothes were made.

Organize the data.

1. What strikes you about your data?

2. What is the **mode** for your data?

3. What is the mode for the class data?

8   Many Points Make a Point: Data and Graphs   EMPower™

Vocabulary words are easy to identify in bold type.

The class **activity** comes next. Often students work with a partner or in a small group.

Practice: Categorically Speaking

Sometimes we can organize categories into subgroups of other categories in order to better understand the data. For example, drug stores will often organize their aisles by category—skin care, beauty aids, and so on. Then the items in each of those aisles are also organized. This makes it easier to take inventory and place orders and for the customer to find products.

Can you think of other examples where information is categorized?

Use the chart below *or* create your own chart; draw a picture; make a list; or write about examples you see at home or at work. In the chart below, one example is given.

Location	What Stuff or Information?	How Is It Organized?
Drug store	Over-the-counter products they sell	Skin care, Beauty aids, Seasonal, Stationery, First aid, Hair care

Practice pages invite students to use new skills.

Extension: Taking Inventory

Find a drawer or closet filled with many things. Use a frequency graph to show the contents. Start with six categories. Then do another frequency graph to show the same items, but this time use three categories.

For example:

My Medicine Cabinet

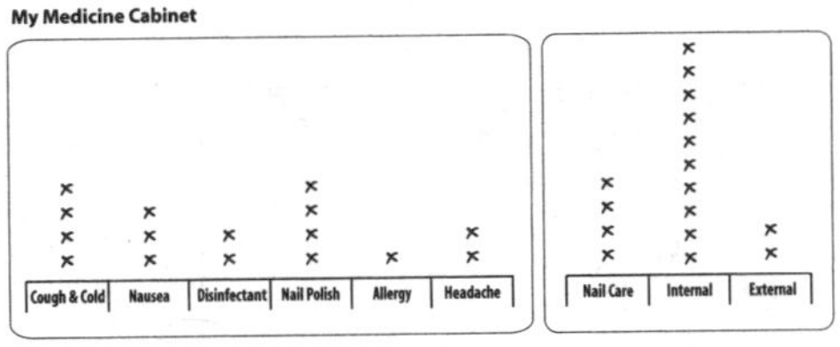

Cough & Cold
Nausea
Disinfectant
Nail Polish
Allergy
Headache
Nail Care
Internal
External

Extension pages present a challenge or a new but related math idea.

Ample space allows students to record most work in their books.

Test Practice

A **Test Practice** that reflects the format of the GED test concludes each lesson.

1. Freda worked at a printing press. She kept a tally of all the defects she found in the books she was processing. Based on the frequency graph she created, shownbelow, which of the following statements is true?

   (1) There were more defects related to colors than any other defect.

   (2) There were twice as many torn pages as there were warped spines.

   (3) There were more warped spines than colors that bled.

   (4) Half of all the defects were related to colors that bled.

   (5) Half of all the defects were related to pages that were torn.

   Book Defects Frequency Graph

Pages Torn	Colors Bled	Uncut Pages	Spine Warped	Faded Colors

2. Tony, a tour guide, has been keeping a tally of visitors from different states. According to his tally, which of the following is *not* a true statement?

   (1) The fewest number of visitors came from Oregon.

   (2) There were as many visitors from Maine as there were from Georgia.

   (3) There were as many visitors from Georgia as there were from Oregon and Texas.

   (4) There were twice as many visitors from Florida as there were from Rhode Island.

   (5) There were twice as many visitors from Idaho as there were from Maine.

   U.S. Tourist Frequency Graph

Florida	Georgia	Idaho	Maine	Oregon	Rhode Island	Texas

3. Clara is paid a commission on each of the large electronics devices that she sells. She tallied the different items she sold for the month. Based on her tally, what can she tell her boss about her sales?

   (1) She sold twice as many DVD players as she did TVs.

   (2) She sold twice as many DVD players as she did computers.

   (3) She sold more DVD players than she did TVs and computers combined.

   (4) She sold more TVs and VCRs than she did stereos and DVD players combined.

   (5) She sold half as many TVs as she did stereos.

   Home Media Frequency Graph

4. Bronson, a forest ranger in the Green Mountains, kept track of the different animals that were reportedly seen in one of the campgrounds during the month of May. Based on his tally, which of the following statements could he tell the media?

   (1) There were twice as many wolves reportedly seen as bears.

   (2) Half of all the reported sightings were wolves.

   (3) There were more bears than wolves reportedly seen.

   (4) There were twice as many moose reportedly seen than there were black bears.

   (5) One-quarter of all reported sightings were brown bears.

   North American Wildlife Frequency Graph

Black Bears	Brown Bears	Moose	Wolves

5. According to Global Exchange, some workers in China who make clothing for Disney are paid as little as $0.16 per hour. At this wage, what amount would a worker make for a 40-hour workweek?

   (1) $64.00

   (2) $6.40

   (3) $6.00

   (4) $80.00

   (5) $0.60

6. In 2003 the U.S. Department of Labor (DOL) issued new regulations for overtime pay. The DOL estimated that under the new regulations 1.3 million low-wage workers would become eligible for overtime pay, unless their wages were raised to $425 per week. The DOL estimated that 24.8 percent of those workers were Hispanic and 16.6 percent were African American. What percent were neither Hispanic nor African American?

Changing the Culture

The authors have created this curriculum to follow the National Council of Teachers of Mathematics (NCTM) Principles and Standards; however, teachers who use EMPower face the challenge of transforming the prevailing culture of their math classrooms. EMPower pilot teachers offer some ideas for facilitating this transition:

- Set the stage. As a class, set ground rules. Explicitly state that this is a space for everyone to learn. As one teacher said, "We are in this together. Share, even if you do not think you are right. Whatever you add will be helpful. It lets us see how you are looking at things."

- Group your students. Match students whose learning styles and background knowledge complement each other. Ask questions, such as How did it go to work together? How did everyone contribute?

- Allow wait time. Studies have shown that teachers often wait less than three seconds before asking another question. Students need more time to think.

- Sit down. Watch students before interrupting to help them. Listen for logic and evidence of understanding. Follow the thread of students' thinking to uncover unconventional approaches. During discussions with the whole group, hand over the chalk.

- Review written work. Look beyond right and wrong answers to learn everything you can about what a student knows. Determine what seems solid and easy, as well as patterns in errors. If students are scattered, suggest ways they can organize their work; this is likely to lead to more efficient problem solving and clearer communication.

- Question. Hearing the right answer is not necessarily a cue to move on. Question students at this point too. Specific questions are included in the lesson facilitation.

Unit Sequences and Connections

The sequence in which the EMPower units can be used effectively with your class will depend on the backgrounds and interests of students. The units are not numbered, so teachers can order them according to their class needs; however, the authors suggest specific unit arrangements that will support students' progression through certain concepts.

The authors do not recommend sequencing the units according to the traditional basic math model that begins with whole numbers and follows with fractions, decimals, and percents; data and graphs; algebra; and then geometry. Instead, they suggest you integrate the five units that focus on numbers with the units on geometry, data, and algebra. The authors found that this integration of topics helped to motivate the adult students in their pilot classes.

Although the units were not specifically designed to build on one another, there are clear connections between some of the units in the series. *Over, Around, and Within: Geometry and Measurement* provides a nice introduction to the program because it focuses on small whole numbers. *Everyday Number Sense: Mental Math and Visual Models* could follow to further develop whole number mental math skills and visual models. *Using Benchmarks: Fractions, Decimals, and Percents* provides the necessary groundwork with fractions, decimals, and percents to describe approximate relationships between data sets in *Many Points Make a Point: Data and Graphs*. And

Split It Up: More Fractions, Decimals, and Percents continues to expand students' repertoire of familiar fractions, decimals, and percents. *Seeking Patterns, Building Rules: Algebraic Thinking* builds upon the tools and relationships used in *Keeping Things in Proportion: Reasoning with Ratios*; finally, *Operations Sense: Even More Fractions, Decimals, and Percents* introduces more complex fractions and operations in geometric, graphic, and algebraic contexts. The following diagram demonstrates this integrated sequence:

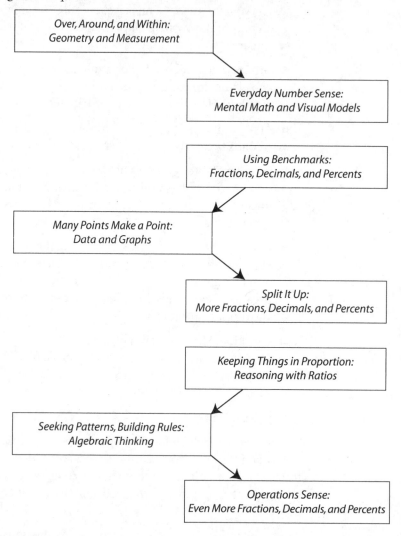

Unit Descriptions

Over, Around, and Within: Geometry and Measurement
Students explore the features and measures of basic shapes. Perimeter and area of two-dimensional shapes and volume of rectangular solids provide the focus.

Everyday Number Sense: Mental Math and Visual Models
Students solve problems and compute with whole numbers using mental math strategies with benchmarks of 1, 10, 100, and 1,000. Number lines, arrays, and diagrams support their conceptual understanding of number relationships and the four operations.

Using Benchmarks: Fractions, Decimals, and Percents
Students use the fractions ½, ¼, ¾, and ¹⁄₁₀; the decimals 0.1, 0.5, 0.25, and 0.75; and the percents 50%, 25%, 75%, 100%, and the multiples of 10% as benchmarks to describe and compare all part-whole relationships.

Many Points Make a Point: Data and Graphs
Students collect, organize, and represent data using frequency, bar, and circle graphs. They use line graphs to describe change over time. They use benchmark fractions and the three measures of central tendency—mode, median, and mean—to describe sets of data.

Split It Up: More Fractions, Decimals, and Percents
Building on their command of common benchmark fractions, students add thirds, eighths, and hundredths and their decimal and percent equivalents to their repertoire of part-whole relationships.

Keeping Things in Proportion: Reasoning with Ratios
Students use various tools—objects, diagrams, tables, graphs, and equations—to understand proportional and nonproportional relationships.

Seeking Patterns, Building Rules: Algebraic Thinking
Students use a variety of representational tools—diagrams, words, tables, graphs, and equations—to understand linear patterns and functions. They connect the rate of change with the slope of a line and compare linear with nonlinear relationships. They also gain facility with and comprehension of basic algebraic notation.

Operation Sense: Even More Fractions, Decimals, and Percents
Students extend their understanding of the four operations with whole numbers as they puzzle over questions such as "How is it possible that two fractions multiplied might yield a smaller amount than either fraction?" and "What does it mean to divide one-half by six?"

Frequently Asked Questions

Q: *I have classes that are widely multi-level. Can this work?*

A: Many teachers see a wide range of levels within the group as an obstacle. Turn the range of levels to your advantage. Focus on students' representations (words, graphs, equations, sketches). This gives everyone the chance to see that answers emerge in several ways. Slowing down deepens understanding and avoids facile responses. Having calculators available can even the playing field. Implement the suggestions in *Making the Lesson Easier* and *Making the Lesson Harder* of each lesson facilitation in the *Lesson Commentary* sections.

Q: *How do I deal with erratic attendance patterns?*

A: Uneven attendance can be disruptive. Students who miss class may feel disoriented; however, the lessons spiral back to the most important concepts. When the curriculum circles back, students will have a chance to revisit concepts and get a toehold.

Q: *What do I do if I run out of time, and there is no way to finish a lesson?*

A: Each activity is important, but reviewing it is equally important. It is better to cut the activity short so there is time to talk with students about what they noticed. Maximize the time by selecting a student or group whose work you feel will add to the class's understanding to report their findings. Be conscious of when you are letting an activity go on too long because the energy is high. Fun is good, but be sure important learning is happening. If you like to give time in class to reviewing homework, and you want to hear from everyone in discussions, you will run out of time. Schedule a catch-up session every three or four lessons.

Q: *How do I respond to comments such as "Can't we go back to the old way?"*

A: Change is unsettling, especially for students who are accustomed to math classes where their job is to work silently on a worksheet solving problems by following a straightforward example. Be clear about the reasons why you have chosen to de-emphasize some of the traditional ways of teaching in favor of this approach. Ultimately, you may need to agree to some changes to accommodate students' input. Meanwhile, stick with the curriculum. Reiterate for students what they have accomplished. When there is an "Aha!" moment, point it out.

Q: *My own math background is not strong. Will I be able to teach this curriculum?*

A: Yes! Most teachers tend to teach the way they were taught. Adopting a different stance requires support, and the more types of support, the better. This curriculum offers support in a few ways. The teacher book for each unit lists open-ended questions designed to keep the math on track. In the *Lesson Commentary* sections, the *Math Background* helps teachers deepen their understanding of a concept. In addition, the *Lesson in Action* sections provide examples of student work with comments that illuminate the underlying mathematics.

The best support often comes from a colleague. If no one at your site is currently teaching EMPower, join the Adult Numeracy Network, http://shell04.theworld.com/std/anpn, and attend your regional NCTM conference. Look for others who are integrating the NCTM Principles and Standards through the use of a curriculum such as *The Investigations in Number, Data, and Space Curriculum* (Russell, S. J., et al., 1998); *Connected Mathematics* (Lappan et al., 1998); or *Interactive Mathematics Program* (Fendel et al., 1997).

Unit Introduction
Over, Around, and Within: Geometry and Measurement

Major Themes

The importance of studying geometry with measurement

Although measurement and the theory behind it can be treated as distinct from geometry, there is much pedagogical value to returning geometry to its roots in spatial measure (National Research Council, 2001, p. 281).

Geometry and measurement pervade our world. At birth, nurses record the weight and length of infants; it is the start of a lifetime filled with measurements. Adults encounter shapes and measurements in art, manufacturing, design, construction, landscaping, cooking, and advertising. When we become actively aware of the organizing principles and relationships governing angles, lines, surfaces, and volumes, we are empowered to plan and maneuver more effectively in space.

Space and size are advertising obsessions in the United States. In the retail and service sectors, people pay for space (for example, booking conference centers and banquet halls). Consumers need the skills to evaluate advertising claims. Is the refrigerator really bigger? Does the floor plan offer more living space, more storage space, or neither? Equally important is whether the bigger appliance will fit in the available space. The unit's integrated approach to geometry and measurement will help adults make more informed decisions in real contexts.

The word "geometry" comes from the Greek words for earth, "geo," and measurement, "metry." Geometry and measurement are subjects that have many mathematical and real-world connections that make them relevant and motivating for students to study.

Geometry and measurement for students at all levels

Geometry provides a platform for visualizing and understanding other areas of mathematics. The principles of counting, number operations, spatial relationships, mathematical reasoning, and algebraic formulations are all present in geometry. Multiplication and addition are employed to find area, perimeter, and volume. Number sense aids in determining missing measurements and arriving at estimates for angle sizes. Reading rulers raises awareness of fractions. Through the study of geometry, adults encounter letters that stand in for numbers, e.g., l for length, h for height, and P for perimeter.

Measurement is often a difficult topic for students to master. Past administrations of the National Assessment of Educational Progress (NAEP) show relatively low performance on measurement problems. While these are assessments of children's understanding, our field-test observations provide evidence that some adults may also have difficulty using everyday tools such as rulers and measuring tapes. The use of measurement tools should be encouraged when adults return to school to work on basic math skills.

The development of an understanding of one-, two-, and three-dimensional space and the distinctions between those three dimensions should also be seen as an important element of basic math courses for adults. Research on geometric understandings shows that, over the years, misunderstandings about the differences among the concepts of distance, area, and volume persist, as does confusion about linear, square, and cubic units; the effect of the length of intersecting lines on the size of angles; and the influence of rotation on shape. By addressing these in the basic math curriculum, students will have a solid foundation to understand formulas, make generalizations, and show proofs.

Visualization, analysis, and informal deduction

The van Heile theory about how children's thinking progresses as they encounter geometry concepts informs the conceptual development of this unit. Pierre M. van Hiele and Dina van Heile-Geldof outlined five levels of understanding (Crowley, 1987):

1. Visualization

2. Analysis

3. Informal deduction

4. Formal deduction

5. Rigor

Over, Around, and Within presents shapes as a starting point for visualization and analysis. Students relate to shapes as configurations of lines and angles, comparing and contrasting these attributes. Students also identify shapes in drawings; recognize similar shapes in various orientations; see shapes within shapes; and describe shapes verbally using informal language and gradually acquiring more formal terminology. As students become familiar with different linear units of measure, they are able to visualize rectangles and rectangular solids from descriptions such as "I have a box 3 inches wide, 5 inches long, and 12 inches deep."

From the outset, the lessons call for students to sketch as a strategy for analyzing shapes. Throughout the unit, sketching is an aid to problem solving and remains one way for students to communicate their reasoning and solutions.

The emphasis in *Over, Around, and Within* rests on informal deduction. Most people who have studied geometry remember formal proofs. However, this method is not the best for the study of geometry because such an approach easily devolves into parroting the logical moves that comprise a proof for a theorem or formula. In EMPower, once students grapple with the concepts, they connect their experience to models, diagrams, and formulas. They justify their solutions and participate in mathematical discussions that demand rigor. Building students' intuitive understanding of area as surface and volume as capacity can short-circuit students' impulsive grasp at a formula. These initial opportunities to visualize, analyze, and reason informally lay the groundwork for further coursework involving more formal reasoning.

Unit Goals

By the end of this unit, students should be able to

- Recognize and describe shapes and their characteristics.

- Find area and perimeter of rectangles and volume of rectangular solids.

- Make drawings to scale.

- Use linear, square, and cubic units.

- Use spatial reasoning to solve problems.

- Make generalizations about two- and three-dimensional shapes.

The Flow of the Unit

This *Teacher Book* provides materials for *Initial*, *Interim*, and *Final Assessments* (see *Assessments*, p. xxiv, for more detail). In broad strokes, students encounter three major themes. During the first four lessons, the emphasis is on sides and angles of polygons. In *Lessons 5–10*, the emphasis shifts to area and perimeter. In *Lessons 11–13*, students explore the volume and surface area of rectangular solids.

Each lesson has one or more activities or investigations. Allowing time for opening and summary discussions (including time for students to write reflections) and assuming a thoughtful pace, most lessons will exceed one hour. Students' reading and writing levels will affect how long each lesson takes.

In *Lessons 1–4*, students

- Use language such as "sides," "parallel," and "perpendicular" to describe and name shapes and their attributes.

- Count sides and angles to compare and contrast shapes.

- Establish a working definition for "angle."

- Use right (90°) and straight (180°) angles as benchmarks to estimate angle size.

- Measure angles with a protractor.

- Use rulers to find perimeter for, enlarge, and measure two-dimensional shapes.

In *Lessons 5–10*, students

- Distinguish between area and perimeter.

- Derive the formulas for area and perimeter.

- Distinguish between similar and nonsimilar shapes.

- Use concrete objects to make sense of unwieldy unit conversions (e.g., 1,296 square inches in a square yard).

In *Lessons 11–13*, students

- Determine capacity of rectangular solids.

- Connect area with volume.

- Contrast surface area and volume.

Materials

The materials needed for each lesson are listed in the *Materials/Prep* section. You will benefit from collecting a variety of objects ahead of time, for example, boxes—such as large paper boxes, shoe boxes, and paper-clip boxes. You also will want to have on hand measuring tools in both metric and customary English units—yardsticks, meter sticks, rulers, and measuring tapes. You might want to order Pattern Blocks™, available from Cuisenaire at: http://www.etacuisenaire.com/. You will also need square-inch tiles and square-foot tiles.

Assessments

Over, Around, and Within opens and closes with assessment, and also includes two interim assessments. These provide multiple ways to gauge what students know and are learning. There are also ongoing assessments in each lesson. These components are described below.

Opening the Unit: Geometry Groundwork

Making a Mind Map: Students record words and ideas they associate with geometry and measurement. By the end of the unit, their Mind Maps will likely include more terms.

Initial Assessment: Students check off "can do," "don't know how," or "not sure" in response to their ability to solve problems, assessing their familiarity with the material as well as their level of confidence. Using the *Checklist*, the *Initial Assessment* yields information on which lessons will be new material and which will be reviews.

Homemade Objects: This activity is appropriate for students at all levels. Students examine, sketch, and identify shapes within an object they have made. This is an informal way to assess what the class already knows about shapes and the vocabulary to describe them. The activity sets the tone for the unit by relating math topics to real-world objects and by welcoming students' expertise in the classroom.

Using Geometry: Students complete a writing sample about using geometry in their lives.

Interim Assessment

Interim Assessment 1: Shapes and Angles covers the content of the first four lessons.

Interim Assessment 2: A Fresh Look covers the content of *Lessons 5–10*. The first activity, *Fixing Up the Classroom*, is a performance assessment in which students apply all they have learned about measuring, finding area and perimeter, converting among units, and drawing to scale. The second activity, *Home, Sweet Home*, is a paper-and-pencil assessment.

Closing the Unit: Design a Box

Design a Box: Students design and describe a box, its dimensions, its surface area, and its capacity to hold multiple, smaller rectangular solids.

Review Session: Students review activities and practice sheets from past lessons and reflect upon what they have learned.

Reflections: Students organize a portfolio showing off their best work and commenting on the lessons that were most challenging.

Mind Map: Students record words and ideas they associate with geometry and measurement. When they compare their Mind Maps with their first efforts, they should see evidence of their increased knowledge and understanding.

Final Assessment: As they did in the *Initial Assessment*, students check off "can do," "don't know how," or "not sure" and then complete tasks and multiple-choice questions, revealing their familiarity with the material as well as their level of confidence. Using the *Checklist*, the *Final Assessment* provides information about which skills are solid and which will need further development.

Ongoing Assessment

Much of the work students do will take place in small groups or pairs. During this time, take the opportunity to look and listen carefully. The *Looking Closely* section of each lesson focuses teachers' attention on progress in four areas:

Concepts: The student grasps major concepts and skills.

Expressive Capacity: The student has the ability to describe, reason aloud, and explain to others. This is easiest to observe in written work, a record with strong evidence of understanding and misconceptions or errors. However, a student's oral remarks are often a more accurate reflection of what he or she knows.

Use of Tools: The student has the ability to use calculators, grid paper, protractors, and rulers to communicate, measure, verify answers, and enrich understanding.

Background Knowledge: The student has the ability to draw upon and share past experiences with construction, measurement, or design to make decisions or predictions.

Many adults have developed their spatial and visual senses. In this unit, they deepen their understanding of geometry and measurement and apply their visual and spatial skills to exploring mathematical questions—the seemingly simple and the more complex, the concrete and the abstract. Completing the unit in its entirety should bring students to a stage where they can apply their knowledge in real-world as well as testing situations.

Facilitating
Opening the Unit:
Geometry
Groundwork

Is there geometry in your life?

Synopsis

This session assesses students' familiarity with basic concepts and vocabulary associated with geometry and measurement. The activities establish a baseline by extending a variety of opportunities for students to interact with and comment on aspects of shapes, including dimensions, angle size, perimeter, area, and volume.

1. Students complete a Mind Map, recording their ideas and associations with geometry and measurement.
2. Students complete a self-assessment based on several problems.
3. Students discuss the geometrical shapes in homemade objects.

Objectives

- Demonstrate prior knowledge of geometry
- Construct an angle demonstrator and record an angle
- Keep a record of vocabulary useful to the study of geometry
- Identify and sketch shapes

Materials/Prep

- Brad fasteners
- Homemade objects and other objects with interesting shapes, such as picture frames, hand-sewn clothes, baked goods, and musical instruments
- Newsprint
- Paper
- Paper-clip boxes
- Rulers marked with centimeters and inches
- Scissors
- Shoe boxes

Ask students to bring homemade objects of their own to class.

Copy angle demonstrators (*Blackline Master 1*) on heavy paper, and cut out two strips per student. This adjustable tool allows students to replicate angles of different sizes.

Make copies of the *Initial Assessment*, p. 161, one for each student.

Opening Discussion

Begin by asking everyone to estimate sizes with their hands:

How big is a foot? A centimeter?

Look around; do we agree?

Provide an overview of the unit, and set the tone for the class. Tell students:

Measurement is key to exploring ideas of geometry, so we will start there. In this class, frequently there will be more than one right answer and many ways to find the answer, yet there also will be times when only one answer will be right.

A centimeter is an example of a standard metric measurement agreed upon by people around the world.

Give some examples of the advantages of standard units of measure:

Every city has a Department of Weights and Measures to monitor and enforce standards. For example, when you buy a gallon of gas, you are assured that every pump at every gasoline station will measure an exact gallon.

Nearly everything constructed by human beings began as a drawing. In this unit, you will learn the geometry useful for planning and designing. You will measure, draw, and plan on paper (in two dimensions) and build, estimate, and measure solids (in three dimensions).

Activity 1: Making a Mind Map

The Mind Map is the first artifact detailing students' prior knowledge of geometry and measurement. By the end of *Opening the Unit*, you should have several artifacts:

- Mind Map (*Activity 1*)
- Students' *Initial Assessment* (*Activity 3*)
- Labeled sketches from *Activity 4: Homemade Objects*
- Writing samples from *Practice: Using Geometry*

Start the Mind Map by writing "Geometry" and "Measurement" on the board. Explain the Mind Map concept:

Mind Maps are an effective way to generate information on a topic when you want to get ideas down quickly. As you brainstorm, you begin to organize ideas by making connections. Remember: When you are brainstorming, there are no wrong answers.

Ask:

Where do you see measurements in your everyday life? What do you know about them?

List some types of measurement units.

What do you know about geometry?

Write down a few ideas. Model clustering them, linking related ideas with lines, and then ask students to record their own ideas on p. 152 of the *Student Book*. After a few minutes, ask students for examples from their work.

As terms related to geometry and measurement arise, start a class vocabulary list. Do not worry about formal definitions; use what students themselves say. You will want to add and refer to this word list, so write it on newsprint. Students can take notes in the *Vocabulary* section of their books, starting on p. 149.

This is an example of one student's mind map:

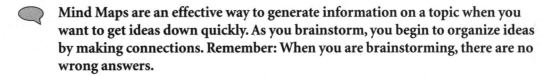

GEOMETRY

multiplication, Fractions, Division, Carefulness, pre-caution, signs, letters (X b a) " quotations, Reading

Activity 2: Making an Angle Demonstrator

Give every student two strips of paper (from *Blackline Master 1*) and a brad fastener. Model making an angle demonstrator. Place one strip on top of the other so the two dots are aligned. Put a fastener through the two dots so the parts can open and close like a mouth. (Directions are also in the *Student Book*, p. 3.) Show students how to use the angle demonstrator by holding it against an angle (for example, the corner of the board); trace the inside lines of the angle demonstrator onto a piece of paper. Tell students they will use their angle demonstrators in the *Initial Assessment* and again in a later lesson.

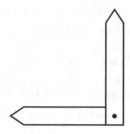

 ## Activity 3: Initial Assessment

Because the *Initial Assessment* can look intimidating, it is recommended that you show the tasks on an overhead projector or otherwise display them for the whole class to see. In addition, distribute a copy of the *Initial Assessment* to every student.

Then explain that this is a test where students do *not* solve the problems. Instead they are to check off "Can do," "Don't know how," or "Not sure" in response to whether they feel they can solve the problem. Tell your students that the results will help you estimate the amount of time they may need on different topics covered in the unit, such as measurement, area, perimeter, and volume.

Show the tasks on the overhead projector. Remind students not to solve the problems, but to assess their confidence in their ability to solve them. Students can read silently or you can read to them. Keep the momentum going, reading the problem and then quickly moving on to the next one.

Collect the assessments and analyze them later.

Heads Up!

If most of your class indicate they can do all of the tasks, and their written work on *Using Geometry* is of high quality, photocopy the *Initial Assessment,* and at the next class meeting ask students to complete the tasks. See *Checklist* (p. 7) for information on instructional decisions.

Activity 4: Homemade Objects

Every student needs an object to complete this activity. There are two options:

- Students can bring homemade objects to class.
- Students can choose an item from your collection.

Refer students to *Homemade Objects, Student Book*, p. 3. Give them time to sketch, identify, and label shapes *within* the object. Some objects will lend themselves better to this activity than others. Convey to students that you do not expect their representations to be perfect.

Model describing how you made one of your own objects. Include geometry terms and the vocabulary of measurement in your description. Then ask students to describe the shapes within their objects.

Summary Discussion

List terms students would like to remember or know more about based on discussions of objects they made or the *Initial Assessment*. If there is time, orient students to their books. They should answer the *Reflection* questions (p. 152). Also have them read through *Unit Goals* (p. 8).

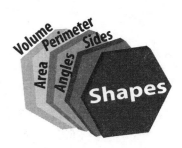

Practice

Using Geometry, p. 5
This is the initial written assessment for the unit. It will be useful to have a sample of each student's work, explaining how he or she sees and uses geometry and measurement.

Seeing Geometry, p. 6
Students choose another object, sketch it, and describe its geometric properties and measurements.

Extension

Name the Shapes, p. 7

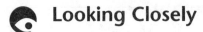

Looking Closely

Observe whether students are able to

Demonstrate prior knowledge of geometry

Do students have experience with this area of mathematics? Do they seem curious?

Construct an angle demonstrator and record an angle

Constructing a measurement tool will help students navigate through the activities of this unit. In addition, it will give you insight into their facility with constructing, aligning, and tracing—skills they will call on as they find area, perimeter, and volume, and record angles. Take note of students who seem adept at this activity; later you can assign students to work in pairs in ways that nurture emerging learners and challenge more advanced students. If some students have difficulty constructing the tools, pair these students with those who have succeeded and can offer help.

Keep a record of vocabulary useful to the study of geometry

Rather than consulting a dictionary, try to piece together definitions based on students' prior knowledge. These definitions can be refined over time.

Do English language learners know geometric terms in their own languages? Ask them to record these as well.

Identify and sketch shapes

Can students identify and name the overall shape of objects? Can they identify and name shapes within objects? Direct students to compare the attributes of shapes, such as length and position of sides and the number and shape of angles (e.g., wide-open or pointy).

WHAT TO LOOK FOR IN *OPENING THE UNIT*	WHO STANDS OUT? (LIST STUDENTS' INITIALS)			NOTES FOR NEXT STEPS
	STRONG	ADEQUATE	NEEDS WORK	
Concept Development • Identifies and names overall shapes of objects • Identifies and names shapes within objects • Compares shapes with other shapes • Records angles using angle demonstrator				
Expressive Capacity • Uses appropriate vocabulary when describing and comparing shapes • Describes shapes within objects with precision				
Use of Tools • Constructs angle demonstrator • Uses angle demonstrator				
Background Knowledge • Is familiar with geometric shapes • Has vocabulary for different shapes, angles, and geometric properties, e.g., area, perimeter, and volume				

Rationale

This lesson is an invitation for students at all levels to discuss shapes, measurements, and the ways in which geometry and measurement contribute to our ability to construct and describe objects. Constructing a measurement tool helps students internalize a sense of angle size. EMPower builds on students' prior knowledge; therefore, objects of students' own making are an ideal starting point.

Math Background

Recognizing the basic shapes—rectangles, squares, circles, and triangles—is critical to the study of geometry and measurement. Observing the characteristics of a shape, such as the number of angles or sides, their relative sizes, and the sides' relative positions, allows us to tap into the established knowledge base about the shape, for example, how to find the measurement for a missing side or angle, or the formula for area.

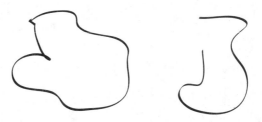

The world is full of squiggly lines and amorphous, incomplete, or open shapes. Open shapes are problematic when determining area. With no clear boundaries, open shapes lead to questions about infinity. Amorphous shapes present a challenge of a different kind. Finding the area of a shape with curves demands making approximations using rectangles, some of which are tiny, to fill in the shape. In calculus, this is done by finding the area under curve through integrals. However, knowing how to find the area of rectangular, triangular, or hexagonal shapes is the first step toward arriving at an estimate of the area or volume of an amorphous shape.

Facilitation

To promote the communication central to mathematics, ask students to interview each other about their homemade objects. Post interview questions such as

💬 **What steps did you take to make the object?**

💬 **What geometric shapes are part of your object?**

💬 **What did you measure?**

💬 **What were the most difficult and enjoyable parts of making the object?**

In some classes, interviewing can be difficult, given the English-proficiency level of the students. Further simplify the task by giving sentence starters, e.g., "I have a _____; I made it by _____."

Teachers and students call on their powers of observation.

Two of my students seemed to wish they had stayed home today, but as they started explaining how they made their objects and measured them, they became engaged in the activity. I noticed one student did not know how to read a ruler. "Rectangle" was not in his vocabulary; he called the cereal box a square and measured the sides to see whether they were the same. The other reluctant student finished drawing his shapes quickly, but the longer he had to wait for his partner to finish drawing, the more he looked at his object, and the more detail he added to his drawing. By the time these two students switched objects to see what the other had missed, the student who was initially resistant was noticing all sorts of things about his partner's object. He tapped into great powers of observation, and then he suddenly looked at the ruler he could not read and started asking questions. He actually figured out ¼ , ½ , and ¾ inches.

Phyllis Flanagan
Rock Valley College Adult Education Center, Rockford, IL

One teacher's homemade item sparks discussion that calls on shape names.

The night before I taught this lesson, I decided to make a heart-shaped cake since it was close to Valentine's Day. Before I went into class, I was thinking about geometry.

I had a box of cake mix, a can of frosting, and square and round pans. I was faced with a few design issues. My plan was to cut the round cake in two and attach the two halves to the square as the humps of the heart. So I had to make sure the side of the square pan was equal to the diameter of the round pan. That was easy. I chose 8-inch pans.

continued on next page

continued from previous page

I asked students to speculate: "What do you think I did to make the cake this shape? What pan(s) do you imagine I used?"

Student: "You used a square pan and cut out a heart."

(I made a mental note that she called the rectangle that she drew a "square"):

Teacher: "That's one way, but that's not how I did it."

Student: "I think you had a big circular pan and cut off pieces. Like this:"

Teacher: "That's another way, but not how I did it."

Student: "You had a heart-shaped pan."

Teacher: "No, but I'll give you a hint. I used two pans, a square one and a round one. Here they are."

(Silence.) Then:

Student: "Okay, I see two parts of the circle, and you pushed the square between them." (He gestured over the cake.)

Teacher: "Yeah, that's exactly what I did. Who's hungry?"

Mary Jane Schmitt
Bridge to Learning and Literacy, Harvard University, MA

1

Sharing Secret Designs

> *What shapes surround you?*

Synopsis

In *Opening the Unit*, students located shapes within objects. In this lesson, using tangible, idealized shapes, students describe the shapes' characteristics, focusing on sides and angles. Angles are explored in more depth in *Lessons 2* and *3*.

1. The whole class describes and names various shapes, recording characteristics and formal and informal names.

2. Students make designs with Pattern Blocks™.

3. In pairs, students give and follow directions for replicating designs.

4. As a whole class, students add descriptions to the shape chart. They identify commonalities and differences among shapes.

Objectives

- Identify characteristics of two-dimensional shapes
- Identify and describe 12 basic shapes

Materials/Prep

- File folders (for concealing secret designs)
- Glue sticks
- Pattern Blocks™
- Shape Set polygons (*Blackline Masters 2* and *3*)

Cut out the set of 12 shapes, and place them in three envelopes. Envelope A contains shapes 2, 3, 9, and 11; Envelope B contains shapes 1, 8, 10, and 12; and Envelope C contains shapes 4, 5, 6, and 7. Make enough envelopes so that each pair of students will have one.

Have ready one Shape Set with masking tape loops on the back of each shape so you can post them on the board as you and students refer to them.

Post the list of vocabulary from *Opening the Unit*.

Prepare a large version of the chart "Shape Descriptions" (*Student Book*, p. 11).

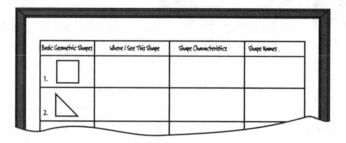

Prepare drawings of two incomplete squares.

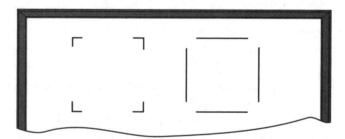

Opening Discussion

Show two versions of an incomplete square. Ask:

> **What do you see? What would you call these parts? (Agree on "angle," or "corner," and "side" to refer to parts of the shape.)**

> **What shapes could I make with these?**

Note that the lines and corners suggest shapes, so our eyes tend to complete the shapes.

Transition to the first activity by saying:

> **In the study of geometry, we will continue to pay close attention to sides and angles, to what is around and within shapes.**

Activity 1: Guess My Shape

Distribute the envelopes with shapes, one per student pair, and ask the students to keep their shapes hidden from partners. Let everyone handle their shapes, still keeping them hidden, as you start the activity.

Read the directions for *Guess My Shape* (*Student Book*, p. 10). Model this activity once, and then assign students to pairs.

Each person takes a turn describing the shape to a partner. The partner sketches and names the shape or asks clarifying yes/no questions to get a better idea of it.

Post the "Shape Description Chart." When most of the student pairs have finished, ask volunteers to fill in the chart with names and characteristics for each shape.

Students take notes on *Shape Descriptions* (*Student Book*, p. 11); or they just listen, and you copy the master for the whole class later. Since there will be opportunities to add to the chart, you may choose not to discuss every shape at length. However, make sure to review the names and characteristics of the basic shapes—the **square, rectangle, hexagon,** and **triangle**. Mark equal sides of shapes with strike marks to show they are equal.

Heads Up!

Treat formal terms lightly; for example, "diamond" is as serviceable a name as **"rhombus."** Students will explore right angles in more depth in Lesson 2. Memorizing the differences between types of triangles is not as important as being able to describe the basic characteristics of the shapes.

If the concept of **parallel** has not yet surfaced, bring it up. Affirm students' informal descriptions of parallel lines. Sketch a model of the **trapezoid** on the board. Have a student extend the four sides with dotted lines so everyone can see the difference between parallel lines (will never intersect or cross) and nonparallel lines (will intersect or cross if continued). Ask students to identify which lines are parallel and which are not. Label the parallel lines.

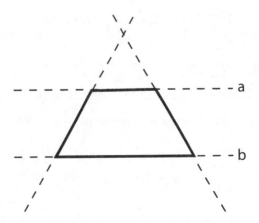

Activity 2: Sharing Secret Designs

Distribute a handful of Pattern Blocks to each pair of students. Review the rules and the goal (*Student Book*, p. 13): One person describes shapes clearly enough for a partner to duplicate the design. (See *Facilitation* for a few variations on the game.) Do one practice design with the whole class.

Pair students. Distribute file folders for keeping individual designs secret.

Heads Up!

English language learners might need a quick review of prepositions—"over," "around," and "within," for example.

Summary Discussion

Bring the class together again and ask:

 What about today's activities was hard? What was easy?

 Were your sketches the same as the original designs? Why or why not?

 What did you notice about particular shapes as you worked with them?

Heads Up!

The last question is essential. Probe here for observations about various shapes.

As students comment, add information to the shape chart. For example:

*   Side relationships: Are they equal lengths? Are they parallel?
*   Types of angles: Are there square corners in the shape? How many are there?

Point out commonalities as well as differences, noting which of the four-sided shapes have parallel sides and which do not. Ask questions such as

 Will you ever see a triangle with parallel sides? Why or why not?

 What shapes can be combined to make another shape?

Allow time for students to reread the information on the chart silently. After *Lessons 2* and *3*, they will be able to add much more about angles. Then direct students to *Reflections* (*Student Book*, p. 152), where they record what they learned about shapes. Volunteers add to the class vocabulary list.

 **Practice**

Road Signs Match, p. 14

Alike Yet Different, p. 15

Covering Hexagons, p. 15.
This is a tactile practice, best done with Pattern Blocks. Alternatively, if students have Internet access, they can go to http://arcytech.org/java/patterns and manipulate the pieces on the computer screen.

 Extension

Hunt for Shapes, p. 17

 Test Practice

Test Practice, p. 18

Looking Closely

Observe whether students are able to

Identify characteristics of two-dimensional shapes

Help students focus on key features of shapes. Place shapes on top of each other. Then compare the shapes and describe each of their characteristics, particularly

- The number of sides and angles in the shape;
- The relationships between sides (are they equal or parallel?);
- Variation in angle size (does the shape have any corners, or what students might term "square angles"?).

Students may count sides excluding the top and bottom. Tell them to keep track of all sides by using a highlighter. Completed shape charts may have personal references, as in the following example.

Basic Geometry Shapes	Shape Name	Shape Characteristics	Where I See This Shape
1.	Square	4 sides 4 90° degree angles	Blocks on the ground Squares on my Remote on the top of my Foyer table
2.	Right triangle/or isosceles	3 = sides 3 Right angles /or 3 90° degree angles	the number 4 on the class Room clock
3.	Rectangle		on my Foyer table the tables in class
4.	Parallelo gram		on my drinking glasses on my Picture Frame
5.	Right triangle scalene		
6.	isosceles triangle	2 sides are equal	at the b

Identify and describe 12 basic shapes

Are students able to distinguish one shape from another? Which shapes and names are familiar? Even familiar shapes can be tricky to define. Help students articulate different ways to describe similarities and differences, e.g., "the short sides are equal in length," or "opposite sides are equal."

Listen to the vocabulary that students use. Does suggesting rhymes or ways to associate names and shapes help? For example, the "x" in hexagon might remind students of the number six (six, sex, hex, hexagon). Allow students to use terms in their native languages if they are English language learners. Gradually increase their comfort with the English words.

Many students are confused by the use of multiple names for one shape. For example, a four-sided figure called a **quadrilateral** can also be a square or a rectangle. Point out that one way to refer to a person is by her name, Mary, but it is equally true that she is a woman, a person, and a mammal. Reviewing the meaning of prefixes such as "bi," "tri," and "quad" may help students remember new words. Brainstorm other words with these prefixes, e.g., "tricycle" and "tripod."

WHAT TO LOOK FOR IN *LESSON 1*	WHO STANDS OUT? (LIST STUDENTS' INITIALS)			NOTES FOR NEXT STEPS
	STRONG	ADEQUATE	NEEDS WORK	
Concept Development • Identifies characteristics of shapes: sides and angles • Distinguishes between shapes • Identifies different types of triangles • Recognizes shapes with more than four sides				
Expressive Capacity • Uses appropriate vocabulary when describing shapes • Compares shapes describing attributes (e.g., parallel lines, right angle)				
Use of Tools • Handles shapes easily, moving them for comparisons • Uses one shape to measure another				
Background Knowledge • Is familiar with geometric shapes • Has vocabulary for different shapes (e.g., right triangle, pentagon, hexagon, octagon, rhombus)				

Rationale

Geometry is visual; it is based on perception and mutual agreement. Most adults already agree that the number 4 stands for four objects, but point to a rectangular-shaped window, and opinions can vary. Some people might look at the inside space; others might look at the frame. Some people might see four angles and four sides defining the edges; others might focus elsewhere. This lesson builds a common language by introducing shape names and vocabulary for describing their characteristics.

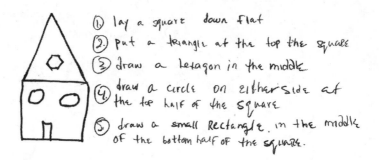

Math Background

The geometry of idealized shapes began with the Greeks, who abstracted ideal shapes from the world around them. They held that a shape of a particular kind has innate unchanging properties or characteristics—that is, a square has four right angles and sides of equal measure, whether it fits on a pinhead or covers acres.

Recognizing the basic shapes—rectangles, squares, circles, and triangles—is critical to the study of geometry. By drawing on what is known about the characteristics of a shape, we can determine the measurement of a missing side or angle, or the formula for area.

Facilitation

For a big class, post enlarged versions of the shapes for everyone to see.

Some alternatives to *Activity 2* follow:

- Begin by making a design and giving directions to students for replicating it.
- Have one volunteer make a design that the whole class works together to replicate.
- Instead of pairs, make groups of four students so that pairs design and guess shapes.
- In groups, have the student who designs answer only yes-no questions posed by those replicating the design.
- Play a simple version where students replicating the design ask direct questions of the designer.

Tell students to check in with you when they think they have replicated a design. In several pilot classes, designers accepted replications that were not exact.

Choose an interesting design presented in class, and ask for suggestions about the best way to give directions for this particular design. Students can amend each other's suggestions.

Making the Lesson Easier

Suggest that students start with a four-shape design.

Making the Lesson Harder

Increase the number of shapes used in *Activity 2: Secret Designs*. Augment with *Irregular Shapes* (*Blackline Master 4*).

Introduce symbols along with vocabulary, e.g., $\parallel$ for "is parallel to," $\perp$ for "is perpendicular to," and $\angle A$ to identify angles.

The activities create a need for a shared lexicon and more precise terms. The class cooperates, sharing vocabulary learned and clarifying their definitions.

> Students were having a good time with the secret design activity, but two groups never seemed to finish. I watched them referring again and again to their vocabulary lists and to the words on the board. All said the hardest part of this activity was saying the names of the shapes, especially the rhombus. Students struggled to express what they saw when they compared angles of shapes. I extended the lines of the sides of the trapezoid and asked what they noticed. Dolores surprised me by stating two sides were parallel. Then Anna asked, "What is the opposite of 'parallel'?" I pointed to the intersecting lines and drew perpendicular lines, so these words were added to the list.
>
> *Roberta Froelich*
> *Middlesex Community College, MA*

> The students loved creating the secret designs and had fun working with each other. When I asked them, I learned more about their focus.
>
> **Teacher:** "What was hard?"
>
> **Student:** "I couldn't understand what my partner was telling me to do. It was easy making my own shape, but it was hard to explain it to someone else without them seeing it."
>
> **Teacher:** "What did you notice about particular shapes as you worked with them?"
>
> **Student:** "Six triangles with the points touching in the middle is a hexagon."
>
> **Student:** "Two triangles make a lazy rectangle (rhombus)."
>
> **Student:** "Two squares make a rectangle."
>
> This was a perfect time in the lesson to talk about parallel lines. One student knew the word "perpendicular" but had it mixed up with "parallel." We discussed both [words] using the pattern blocks.
>
> *Andrea Parrella*
> *Gila Crossing Community School, AZ*

Get It Right

> ### *At what angle is reading comfortable?*

Synopsis

After determining the number of angles in a shape in *Lesson 1*, students focus on angles, angle types, and angle relationships in *Lessons 2* and *3*.

1. On their own, students look for angles in objects. With a partner, they compare the relative size of angles.

2. The whole class shares observations, coming to a working definition of an angle.

3. The whole class demonstrates and discusses 90° angles, as well as angles that are less than and greater than 90°. Angle labeling is introduced.

4. Using their angle demonstrators, pairs of students investigate whether everyone holds a book at the same angle to read.

5. Students compare their angles for holding a book while reading and figure out a good angle for a cookbook stand.

6. Students end the lesson by thinking about situations where the size of the angle would be important.

Objectives

- Identify and describe an angle
- Estimate angle size using the benchmark of 90°
- Use a protractor to measure angles
- Use conventional notation for angles

Materials/Prep

- A carpenter's square, available at hardware stores, is highly recommended.

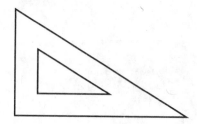

- Angle demonstrators
- Blank sheets of paper, one per student
- Clipboards, one per pair, can be improvised from cardboard
- Pencils
- Protractors (If you do not have easy access to protractors, copy the ones pictured on *Blackline Master 5* onto transparencies and cut them out.)
- Rulers

Collect and bring to class objects with angles—for example, a door wedge, a spatula, scissors, chopsticks, a compact mirror, a 3" x 5" note card; also postcards, photos, or stamps with imagery featuring angles.

Make an overhead or carefully copy onto the board the angles pictured on *Blackline Master 6* for the *Opening Discussion*.

Copy activity instructions (*Student Book,* p. 20); then tape or clip them to the clipboards.

Opening Discussion

In the course of introducing angles, be sure to

- Have students identify angles in objects;
- Define angles; and
- Bring up and correct misconceptions about angles.

Display an assortment of objects. Invite students to choose one. Tell students they are each to

- Find an angle in their object or picture;
- Share with a neighbor the angle they see; and
- Compare their angle with a partner's. Is one larger than the other, or are they the same?

Ask for and record a few observations about angles in the objects.

 When you and your partner compared angles, how were your angles the same? How were they different?

Confront a common misconception by drawing two sets of equal angles on the board.

Tell the class:

💬 **Mathematicians say these angles are equal. How are they the same?**

Acknowledge that line length can be deceptive; however, angle size depends on the space between the sides, not the length of the sides.

💬 **What is an angle?**

Reach a working definition of an angle, for example, the rotation between two lines joined at a point called the **vertex**. Accept informal language if it is accurate.

Heads Up!

It is helpful to use a carpenter's square when you or students are verifying that an angle is a right angle because it can easily be turned to different orientations.

Draw attention to the "square angles" or "corners" on one of the objects, and tell the class that this is a **right angle**, or a 90° angle.

Form a 90° angle with your hands, and ask students to do likewise. Then form one with your forearms. Compare the two right angles—one will look bigger—and ask:

💬 **How can these both be right angles?**

Students can check a few more right angles around the classroom with either a piece of paper or a carpenter's square. Then distribute angle demonstrators once the class seems sure about the benchmark. Ask for a 90° angle demonstration, and direct students to look around the room at each other's angles. Ask:

💬 **How do you know what you are seeing is a right angle?**

Display *Blackline Master 6*, or draw the following angles on the board.

Ask:

Which of these are right angles? How do you know?

Use a corner of a piece of paper to verify which angles are right angles. Mention that a right angle is not right as in "right and left," but rather is the correct angle for building straight walls.

Ask whether anyone knows how to indicate a right angle in math drawings (└) or how 90° is written using the degree symbol (°). Choose volunteers to mark and label each right angle you drew on the board. Ask students whether they know what **perpendicular** lines are. If they do not, define them, and let students find examples in the room.

Refer again to the angle drawings and ask:

Which of these angles is not a right angle?

Name the angles larger than 90° "**obtuse**" and those smaller than 90° "**acute**." Ask students to use their angle demonstrators to show an angle that is more than 90° and one that is less than 90°.

Then ask:

What changes when the angle is less than 90°?

Students sketch the angles on the board. Show how to label non-right angles with an arc and a letter.

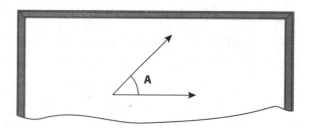

Volunteers label the angles you and they drew. Explain that this notation will be used during the next exercise.

Reiterate the main ideas, saying:

An angle measures 90° when the lines of the angle are perpendicular to each other. If the lines are closer together, they form an angle less than 90°, an acute angle; when the lines are open wider, that angle, greater than 90°, is obtuse.

Transition to the activity by saying:

Angle size affects how machines work and how our bodies function.

Activity: What Is a Comfortable Angle?

Heads Up!

Do not pass out protractors until needed. Students will benefit from first building an intuitive sense of angle size.

Tell students that you have observed them either bending over a book to read or tipping it up.

 This makes me wonder. If I were going to design a book holder, at what angle would I set the stand?

Listen to some ideas. Distribute the clipboards, and read aloud and model the instructions for *Activity: What Is a Comfortable Angle?* (*Student Book*, p. 20).

Heads Up!

Because the directions are detailed, model them step by step as they are read. Suggest students trace the angles using the inside edge of the angle demonstrator because the vertex of the outside angle is not well formed. Remind students that they do not need to trace the full length of the demonstrators.

Distribute a blank sheet of paper to each student. Partners trace the angles for one another, using their angle demonstrators. Suggest pairs look at angles others have traced and compare what they see with their own.

Draw the class back together. Every pair should have examined at least one other pair's angles before you start a brief discussion.

 What did you notice about the angles?

Introduce the protractor. (See *Looking Closely*, p. 26, for ideas.) Students continue the activity working with their personal ∠A and ∠B.

Allow a few minutes for students to measure the angles they traced. Afterward, pairs post their measurements on the board under headings: Angle A (comfortable)—Angle B (impossible). Ranges for Angle A are usually 40°–70°, and for Angle B, most measurements are 90° or more.

When all students are finished, review the numbers for Angles A and B.

 Now that you have looked at and measured comfortable angles for reading (∠ A), what can you conclude?

If any students know how to find an average, ask them to find it for Angle A. Listen to a few remarks about the average. Then ask:

What statements can you make about the angles at which it became impossible to read?

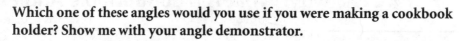

Which one of these angles would you use if you were making a cookbook holder? Show me with your angle demonstrator.

Summary Discussion

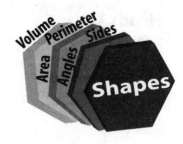

Direct the class to *Reflections* (*Student Book,* p. 152), where they list what they learned and what they would still like to know about angles.

In what other situations would the size of the angle be important?

Add new words to the class vocabulary list, especially: angle, right angle, perpendicular lines, and obtuse and acute angles.

Practice

Sign on the Line, p. 22
For practice estimating and measuring angles.

Less Than, Greater Than, Equal to 90°, p. 23

Shapes and Angles, p.25.

Extension

90°, p. 26
For practice with complementary angles.

Degrees of Comfort, p. 27

Test Practice

Test Practice, p. 28

Looking Closely

Observe whether students are able to

Identify and describe an angle

Note what students focus on as they look for angles. When the angle is in a two-dimensional (2-D) representation, direct attention to the shape first, identifying all its internal angles. Students can lay their angle demonstrators on top of angles they are measuring or fit them in to make the angles more visible.

A working definition of angle should emerge with students agreeing on the sweep of space (or just "the space") between two lines. Some students may recall a definition about two lines joined at a point; be sure to distinguish between the two lines and the space they define. If students rely on the word "corner" to refer to angles, draw an angle that is nearly 180° and ask about it being a corner. Stress that all angles are not obvious corners. Reach a shared definition for "corner" if students use the word frequently.

Estimate angle size using the benchmark of 90°

Provide opportunities to overlap and trace angles of different sizes, including 90° angles and those greater and less than 90°. Use a book to demonstrate by holding the cover open at different angles.

Use a protractor to measure angles

Most students love to use the protractor, but many have trouble remembering how. Allow plenty of time for practice. Recommend students make a list of steps for themselves as a reference. This list should include at least three steps, such as (1) decide whether the angle is less than, greater than, or equal to 90°; (2) place the center mark of the protractor on the point where the angle lines meet; and (3) line up the protractor's line or 0° mark with one line of the angle.

Use conventional notation

Reinforce students' sense of notation by labeling angles whenever you refer to them. You should be able to distinguish between each student's right-angle and non-right-angle marks even if the marks are not truly square. You might assure the class that standard tests label right angles so no assumptions are necessary.

WHAT TO LOOK FOR IN *LESSON 2*	WHO STANDS OUT? (LIST STUDENTS' INITIALS)			NOTES FOR NEXT STEPS
	STRONG	ADEQUATE	NEEDS WORK	
Concept Development • Recognizes angles • Identifies 90° angles • Recognizes angles greater than and less than 90°				
Expressive Capacity • Defines angle • Uses appropriate vocabulary when describing right, acute, and obtuse angles • Uses angle notation				
Use of Tools • Handles the angle demonstrator • Uses protractor to get accurate measurements				
Background Knowledge • Knows what a right angle is from prior experience • Has vocabulary for different angles: right, acute, and obtuse				

Rationale

Angles are used to describe shapes and to build and design objects, functional and artistic. Ninety-degree angles provide a benchmark for estimating the size of other angles. By practicing eyeballing right angles, as well as angles larger and smaller than 90°, students build an intuitive sense of angle size. Perpendicular lines and the conventional notation for a right angle are ways to indicate a 90° angle; these cues help establish the measurements of other angles.

Math Background

To isolate what makes an angle an angle, think about the meeting point of two lines forming a rotation. The lines and vertex—the point where the two lines forming the angle meet—are essential, but what is measured is the rotation or the sweep of space. Angles can look static or bounded, as they do inside shapes, or they can look more dynamic, with their rays extended. The word "angle" comes from Latin for "corner."

Right angles play a special role in geometry. They are formed when two perpendicular lines meet at a 90° angle. They can be seen at corners, doors, windows, outlet covers, books, computers, and more.

Facilitation

Making the Lesson Easier

Take two sessions to complete the activities. Devote more time to looking for, comparing, and tracing angles in pictures and objects in the classroom.

Making the Lesson Harder

Start the lesson with *Activity 2*. Then assign *Extension: 90°* (*Student Book*, p. 26).

Students relate angle sizes to the 90° benchmark.

Esther wore her "geometry outfit." She started class by asking students to name the shapes on her sweater and her argyle socks as a way to review.

A student showed off, telling the class: "I made a 45° angle."

Teacher: "How do you know it is 45°? Can you draw it so we can all see?" (To the class): "How did he get it?"

Student: "He started with a 90°."

Student: "He multiplied." (Pause) "No, he divided."

Teacher (to the student drawing the 45° angle): "How did you know?"

Student: "I cut it in half. Half of 90 is 45."

Teacher: "So how do we know when an angle is less than 90°?"

Student: "Anything more tipped—or more slanted—is less than 90°."

Later, when synthesizing the list of "A" angles the teacher asked:

Teacher: "What do you notice about 'A' angles? What can we say about them?"

Student: "Everybody's is different."

Student: "Angle A is the smallest."

Student: "Angle A is less than all of them."

Student: "B is more than 90°."

Student: "Angle A is a little less than 90°."

Student: "B is more than 90°."

Teacher: "Is it a lot more or a little more?"

Student: "A lot more."

(The teacher asks which angle would be used for a podium and has a student draw it on the board. The class discusses it and then summarizes.)

Teacher: "Why are angles so important? Where do you see that?"

Student: "Because of airplanes—how they take off."

Student: "Buildings."

Teacher: "Where are the angles in a building?"

Student: "The roof . . . for releasing the rain. Ramps. Escalators."

Student: "Nothing is right unless the angle is right and the numbers are correct."

Esther D. Leonelli, observed by Tricia Donovan
Notre Dame Education Center, South Boston, MA

Get It Straight

> *Where do you see straight angles?*

Synopsis

In the previous lesson, students used 90° as a benchmark and measured angles. In this lesson, the last dedicated solely to angles, the focus is on straight (180°) angles.

1. The whole group reviews 90° angles and explores a straight angle.

2. Student pairs use two angle demonstrators to determine that a straight angle measures 180°.

3. Students tear off the three angles of triangles and align them to discover that the angle measurements total 180°.

4. Student pairs visit stations to explore total angle measurements in other triangles and rectangles.

5. Students explain how knowing one angle's measurement helps determine missing information about other angles in a line, triangle, or rectangle.

Objectives

- Identify a 180° angle, singly or as a combination of angles
- Prove that the sum of the angles in a triangle is 180°
- Prove that the sum of the angles in a rectangle is 360°

Materials/Prep

- Angle demonstrators
- Calculators
- Markers or masking tape

- Rulers
- Scissors
- Scotch tape or glue sticks

- Newsprint
- Yardstick
- Protractors

Make copies of the scalene triangles, *Blackline Master 7*, one for each pair of students.

Set up five stations for *Activity 2*. Make duplicate stations if you have a large class. Details about station set up and what happens at each station are as follows:

Station 1: Triangles

Make enough copies of *Blackline Master 8* so that there is one triangle for each student. Cut out the triangles. Post one example of each triangle on the wall by Station 1. Make a long line on newsprint, using masking tape or a marker, and post this also. Students tape their torn angles on this line.

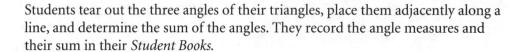

Students tear out the three angles of their triangles, place them adjacently along a line, and determine the sum of the angles. They record the angle measures and their sum in their *Student Books*.

Station 2: Rectangles

Make enough copies of *Blackline Master 9* so that there is one rectangle for each student. Cut out the rectangles. Post one example of each rectangle on the wall by Station 2. Make another long line on newsprint and post; students tape their torn angles on this line.

Students tear out the four angles of their rectangles, place them adjacently around the point on the line, and determine their sum. They record the angle measures and their sum on p. 31 of the *Student Book*.

Station 3: Personal Triangle

Set up the station with blank paper, rulers, and scissors. Make another long line on newsprint and post.

Students create their own triangles and trace them. Then they cut out one of their triangles, tear out its angles, and place them along the line to determine their sum.

Station 4: At the X

Use a yardstick to mark a large X on newsprint. Make the angles as close to 60° and 120° as possible. Leave protractors at the station.

Students measure one angle and determine the measurements of the other angles in the X.

Station 5: Triangle Types

Copy and cut out the set of nine cards, *Triangle Types, Blackline Master 10*.

Students sort the triangles according to their type: right, isosceles, equilateral, or scalene.

Opening Discussion

Start with a quick review. Distribute angle demonstrators.

💬 **Where do you see 90° angles?**

After students point out 90° angles, say:

💬 **Use your demonstrators to show me a right angle.**

💬 **Now I need two people to hold their angles back to back.**

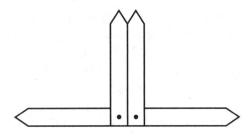

Gradually open your own angle demonstrator to a 180° angle. Hold it alongside the students' back-to-back right angles.

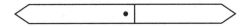

💬 **This looks like a straight line. According to our definition for an angle from the last class, is this an angle? How do you know?**

Review the definition and ask:

💬 **What is the measurement of this straight angle?**

Ask a volunteer to measure the angle with a protractor.

💬 **So, 90° and 90° is 180°. What are some other angle combinations that could make a 180° angle?**

Listen to several combinations. The 90° angle was the first benchmark angle students worked with. Now they have another: the180° angle. Reinforce both benchmark angles by asking students to form a right angle with their arms and then a straight one. Ask them what the difference is. Make a real-world connection.

💬 **What does it mean to "do a one-eighty" when driving or to undergo a 180-degree turn in your opinion?**

Ask a volunteer to physically act out the phrases.

Then make the transition to the activity by saying:

💬 **Knowing what a right angle looks like or that a straight line measures 180° is helpful when solving problems.**

💬 **Many shapes have angles. Some are even named by their angles. For example, "triangle" means three angles. These three angles, as we will soon see, have some special characteristics.**

Activity 1: Angles in Triangles

Introduce the characteristics and names of the triangle types: right, isosceles, equilateral, and scalene. (See *Math Background*, p. 39, for descriptions). Use the posted triangles from the Shape Set as examples. Add words and definitions to the class vocabulary list, but do not spend too much time at this. Students will see the terms again at Station 5.

Distribute copies of scalene triangles (*Blackline Master 8*) to each pair of students. Ask them to describe the characteristics of the triangle and name its type.

Demonstrate labeling and tearing off the angles of a triangle and taping them onto a 180° angle with the labeled angles facing in and the torn or cut sides facing out. All angle pieces should be next to each other, each point touching the vertex and all points fitting together with no gaps or overlaps.

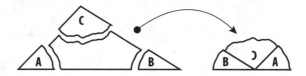

Refer students to *Activity 1: Angles in Triangles, Student Book*, p. 30. After they have a chance to tear their triangles and fit their own angles on the line, ask:

 What can you say about the total measurement of the angles of this triangle?

Heads Up!

Encourage students to situate one angle on the line and to tape it before placing the second and then the third.

Ask:

 Will all these triangles have a total angle measure of 180°? Does anyone think different triangles will have different angle totals? In the next activity, we will find out.

 ## Activity 2: On the Line

Refer students to *On the Line* (*Student Book*, p. 31). Assign students to pairs or groups, and direct them to travel to each of the five stations, following the directions at each one. Students may start at any station. They should record their findings on pp. 31 and 32 of the *Student Book*.

Refer to *Materials/Prep* for details about the materials needed to set up each station and what happens at each one.

Summary Discussion

Review findings for Stations 1 and 3. Ask students:

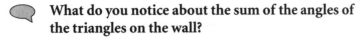 **What do you notice about the sum of the angles of the triangles on the wall?**

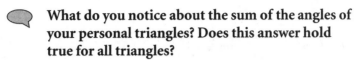 **What do you notice about the sum of the angles of your personal triangles? Does this answer hold true for all triangles?**

Ask for a summary statement:

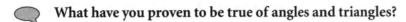 **What have you proven to be true of angles and triangles?**

Prompt for a rule stated in a complete sentence, and post the rule.

Make a huge triangle and a tiny triangle on the board. Ask:

What is true about the sum of the measurements of the angles in each of these two triangles?

Review findings for Station 2. Draw a huge rectangle and ask:

What can you say about the sum of the angles in this rectangle?

Review findings for *Station 4: At the X*. Ask:

How did knowing the measurement of one angle along the line help you figure out the measurements of the other angles?

Review the work on the chart at *Station 5: Triangle Types*. If students had different opinions about any of the triangles, discuss characteristics of the triangles.

Help students make a connection among the work done at the five stations by presenting triangles of different types and asking students to deduce the measurements of the missing angles.

Remind students that they can indicate when sides of a triangle have the same length by using tick marks like this:

Sketch and label the triangles as shown, and pointing to each one, ask:

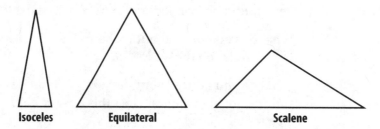

Isoceles   **Equilateral**   **Scalene**

 **In this isosceles triangle, we know that this angle measures 20°. What are the measures of the other two angles? How do you know? Will this always be the case?** (Yes, the steps to find the missing angle measurements will always be the same; no, isosceles triangles will not always have one 20° and two 80° angles.)

 **In this equilateral triangle, no angle measurements are given. What are the measures of the angles? How do you know? Will this always be the case?**

 **In this scalene triangle, we know that this angle measures 40°. What are the measures of the other two angles?** (Not enough information is provided to determine the other two angles.) **Is this always true?**

 **Can a triangle ever have more than one right angle? Why?**

 **Can an equilateral triangle have a right angle? Why?**

 **Can a triangle be both isosceles and a right triangle? Why?**

Close by noting that straight and right angles are good tools for finding unknown angle measurements, and emphasize again that the sum of the angles of a triangle is always 180°. Refer students to *Reflections* (*Student Book*, p. 153), where they record what they learned about straight angles and triangles and what questions they still have.

Practice

Missing Angle Measures, pp. 33

Angles and Roads, pp. 34

Quilted Triangles, p. 36
For more practice identifying equilateral, isosceles, and right triangles.

Measure It Up, p. 37

Extension

Hunting for Angles in the Real World, p. 38

Test Practice

Test Practice, p. 39

Looking Closely

Observe whether students are able to

Identify a 180° angle, singly or as a combination of angles

If students have trouble understanding that a straight angle measures 180°, encourage them to use a protractor. Some students might benefit from kinesthetic reinforcement. They can make two angles with their hands, 0°and 90°, and combine two 90° angles to form a 180° angle. They can also find 180° angles in the classroom and trace them with their fingers.

Using a protractor will also be helpful for finding that the angles in a triangle total 180°. If students remain unconvinced after the angle tear-and-tape activity, suggest they use protractors to measure the angles. Seeing that the angles, taken directly from the triangle, equal a straight angle when put side by side will help students remember that the sum of the measurements of the angles of any triangle is 180°.

Because the straight angle appears as a straight line, it can be confusing for students who are just learning to think of an angle as the space between two lines joined at a vertex. For the moment, continue to highlight the vertex when drawing straight angles.

Understanding supplementary angles (angles that add up to 180°) is as much a number issue as it is a geometry issue. Let students who are struggling use calculators.

Prove that the sum of all angles in a triangle is 180°

Look for students who can generalize from the angle-tearing activity to state the rule. Verifying answers in multiple ways is a useful skill. Have students use protractors to measure all the angles in the triangles if they want to verify the tearing activity. After measuring, ask them to revisit the tearing activity. If needed, have them repeat the activity with several triangles to find the sum of the angle measures.

Prove that the sum of the angles in a rectangle is 360°

Ask students to show how they saw the 360°. When the angles of the rectangle are placed together, students may see the 360° in different ways, as shown below:

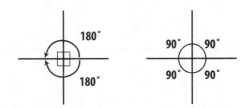

Some may see the 90° + 90° + 90° + 90° adding up, or four x 90. Others may see the 180° + 180°. Ask students to investigate whether the sum of the angles of all four-sided polygons would total 360°.

WHAT TO LOOK FOR IN LESSON 3	WHO STANDS OUT? (LIST STUDENTS' INITIALS)			NOTES FOR NEXT STEPS
	STRONG	ADEQUATE	NEEDS WORK	
Concept Development • Recognizes 90° angles • Recognizes that a line forms a 180° angle • Generalizes that the sum of two right angles is 180° • Generalizes that the sum of the angles of a triangle is 180° • Generalizes that the sum of the angles of a rectangle is 360°				
Expressive Capacity • Uses appropriate vocabulary when describing triangles: right, isosceles, equilateral, and scalene • Articulates a rule based on evidence				
Use of Tools • Handles the angle demonstrator • Uses the protractor to measure angles • Combines all angles to form a straight line				
Background Knowledge • Identifies 90° angles • Recognizes a line • Has vocabulary for different triangles: right, isosceles, equilateral, and scalene				

Rationale

Like the 90° angle, the straight angle is a benchmark in mathematics. Though not as obviously angular as other angles, the straight angle—or line—occurs as an idiom in everyday language, as in "I did a 180-degree turn." In test-taking situations, students can rely on 180° as a clue to determine other angle measures.

Math Background

The 180° angle is frequently included in mathematics lessons about supplementary, vertical, and alternate angles. Supplementary angles are angles that add up to 180°. For example:

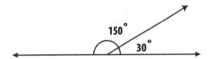

On one line, it is easy to see the two angles whose measures add up to 180°. But what happens when two lines intersect, as seen here?

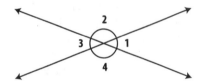

There are interesting relationships among the angles formed by the two intersecting lines. First, there are four pairs of adjacent supplementary angles. Adjacent angles share a side, just as adjacent rooms share a wall. In this diagram, the sum of the degrees of any two adjacent angles is 180° because they lie on a straight line. The sum of the measures of $\angle 1$ and $\angle 2$ is 180°, as are the sums of the measures of $\angle 2$ and $\angle 3$, $\angle 3$ and $\angle 4$, and $\angle 1$ and $\angle 4$.

The second interesting relationship is between the vertical angles, or the angles that are nonadjacent ($\angle 1$ and $\angle 3$, as well as $\angle 2$ and $\angle 4$). Vertical angles are always equal. In this case, the vertical angles form inverted V's. A formal proof for the equality of vertical angles is

$m\angle 2 + m\angle 3 = 180°$
(They form a straight line.)

$m\angle 1 + m\angle 2 = m\angle 2 + m\angle 3$
(This illustrates the transitive property of equality.)

$m\angle 1 = m\angle 3$
(If $a + b = c + b$, then $a = c$.)

This can be investigated less formally in class. (Note that the formal way to indicate "measure of angle 2" is "$m\angle 2$". In this less formal unit, the "m" is not used often.

Another situation commonly seen in high school geometry books occurs when two parallel lines are cut by a transversal. In this diagram, the transversal makes four angles with each of the parallel lines.

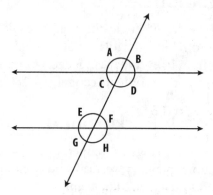

There are eight pairs of adjacent supplementary angles in this situation (e.g., ∠A and ∠B). There are four pairs of vertical angles (e.g., ∠B and ∠C).

Given just one angle measurement, it is possible to figure out the measurements of the other three angles formed on the first parallel line by using what is known about supplementary and vertical angles. This situation occurs again on the second parallel line, where the two angles are corresponding angles because they are positioned at equivalent places. For example, ∠A and ∠E are corresponding angles, as are ∠D and ∠H. Corresponding angles are equal, so ∠A and ∠E are equal, as are the other three pairs of corresponding angles.

Two angles are alternate interior angles if (1) they are in the middle part of the diagram (e.g., ∠C, ∠D, ∠E, and ∠F); (2) they are on opposite sides of the transversal; and (3) if one angle is from the angles on one of the parallel lines, and the other is from the angles on the other parallel line (i.e., one is ∠A, ∠B, ∠C, or ∠D; the other is ∠E, ∠F, ∠G, or ∠H). In the diagram above, therefore, ∠C and ∠F are alternate interior angles, and ∠D and ∠E are another pair of alternate interior angles. Like the corresponding angles, alternate interior angles are equal. That is, ∠C and ∠F are equal.

Two angles are alternate exterior angles if (1) they are in the outer part of the diagram (i.e., ∠A, ∠B, ∠G, and ∠H); (2) they are on opposite sides of the transversal; and (3) one angle is from the angles of one on the parallel lines, and the other is from the angles on the other parallel line (i.e., one is ∠A, ∠B, ∠C, or ∠D; the other is ∠E, ∠F, ∠G, or ∠H). In the diagram above, therefore, ∠A and ∠H are alternate exterior angles, and they are equal, as are the other three pairs. Students can explore this situation informally, with or without the vocabulary.

The type of triangle you give to students so they can tear off angles and determine their sums is not important. In fact, it is useful to give students a variety of triangles so they can see that it does not matter what type the triangle is; the total angle measure is always 180°. Reinforce vocabulary when describing the triangles so students hear and use the words and can learn some of the prefixes: *equilateral* (all angles have equal measure and all sides are equal); *isosceles* (two angles have equal measure and two sides are equal); *right* (one right angle); and *scalene* (no two angles or sides are equal).

Context

To make a language connection, discuss expressions that refer to angles.

💬 **What's your angle?**

💬 **His attitude changed 180 degrees.**

💬 **The car did a three-sixty on the highway.**

Facilitation

If your class is familiar with "Number of the Day," use this format as a catalyst for students to name combinations of numbers that total 180. Students share ways to arrive at the number 180 using addition, subtraction, multiplication, or division, alone or in combinations.

Making the Lesson Harder

Ask students to explore the sum of the angles of a pentagon (five-sided figure), a hexagon, and other polygons and to look for patterns. Suggest they use a table to keep track of the number of sides of the polygon, the number of angles, and the sum of the angles.

While introducing the straight angle, one teacher made many references to "doing a one-eighty."

Teacher: "Tell me when I have 'done a one-eighty.'"

Student: "When you turn back the way you came." (Teacher demonstrates by turning about face.)

Student: "Oh, I didn't know that. That is a common sense thing, isn't it?"

Teacher: "So what is the term in the army when you are marching and they want you to turn around and go back the way you came?"

Students (in chorus): "About face."

Teacher: "And what about when we say someone's attitude did a one-eighty?"

Student: "He was mean and then so nice."

Student: "He did a direct turn-around."

Teacher: "So how many 90° turns do I do to make 'a one-eighty'?"

Student: "Do only two turns."

The teacher drew a straight line bisected by a perpendicular line and drew arrows showing each 90° turn taken to reach 180°. She then wrote on the board that $\angle 1 = 90°$ and $\angle 2 = 90°$, so $\angle 1 + \angle 2 = 180°$.

At the end of the lesson, students summarized:

Student: "A straight angle is a line."

Student: "A straight angle is 180°."

Student: "If you do a 180°turn, you go back to where you came from."

Student: "All triangles equal up to 180°, even if they look different."

Student: "Yeah, even if some are pointy."

Esther D. Leonelli, observed by Tricia Donovan
Notre Dame Education Center, South Boston, MA

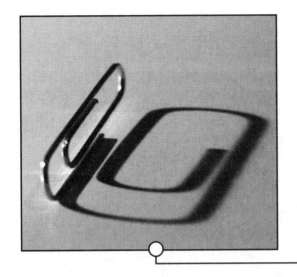

Giant-Size

> ## *How do the shapes compare?*

Synopsis

This lesson introduces two ideas: similar shapes and perimeter. Perimeter is further explored in *Lessons 5, 6,* and *7.* Drawing to scale, an application of similarity, is covered in *Lesson 10.*

1. The class examines and describes the relationship between a rectangular business card and a dissimilar, enlarged version.

2. In groups, students construct enlargements of two-dimensional objects, such as a dollar bill, and measure the dimensions of the original and enlarged shapes.

3. The whole class revisits the concepts of similarity and perimeter and the procedures for determining them.

Objectives

- Identify width and length as dimensions
- Use a ruler or a meter stick marked in centimeters to measure width and length
- Identify similar shapes using spatial comparisons and dimension measurements
- Find perimeter by adding the lengths of the sides

Materials/Prep

- Angle demonstrators
- Calculators
- Measuring tools in centimeters
- Newsprint
- Ribbon, yarn, or colored tape

Cut out and post business cards and flyer, *Blackline Masters 11* and *12*.

Assemble the following objects, enough for one object per pair. On the back of each object, attach a Post-it Note™ with the number of times the object will be enlarged. Ideas for the giant-size activity are as follows:

- Small envelope (gift-card size), enlarged 10 times
- Dollar bill, enlarged 6 times
- Floppy disk or CD cover, enlarged 5 times
- Scarf, handkerchief, or bandana, enlarged 3 times
- Seed packet, enlarged 6 times
- Matchbook, enlarged 10 times
- Three-sided or irregular four-sided items for more advanced students (food pyramid, oddly shaped earring or pendant)

Prepare an answer sheet with the original and enlarged dimensions for each object, so students can check their work.

Prepare and post a sheet of newsprint where all data can be recorded and examined:

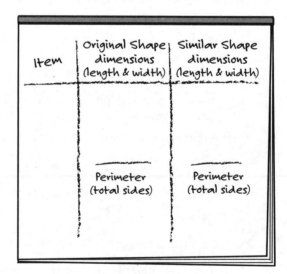

Opening Discussion

Use a business card and an enlarged but not mathematically similar version of the card as a catalyst for discussing what makes shapes similar. Show a business card that has been enlarged to be a flyer and say:

> **I asked for this card to be enlarged and turned into a flyer. I wanted the flyer to be similar to the original card, and it came back like this. I told the printer, "Do it over again." Why?**

Draw attention to the shape and its attributes by asking:

> **What has changed?**

> **Have the angles changed?**

Make sure to emphasize that the angles stayed the same.

> **What about the sides?**

As students contrast the two images, they should note where distortion has occurred. Emphasize the features that are critical when considering similarity: dimensions of width and length (each enlarged or reduced by the same factor, for example, 1/2 or 10), and angle size (kept the same or unchanged).

Model the use of the terms "**length**" and "**width**" and measure both dimensions. Ask volunteers to assist. Review the procedures for linear measurement, such as lining up the ruler and finding zero or compensating if students prefer to start at "1"; and converting to centimeters if more than one unit of measurement is given.

Introduce the terms "**similarity**" or "**similar shapes**" by asking:

> **What would have to be true for the new version to be an accurate enlargement? What would make it similar to the original?**

The mathematical ideas to emphasize are

- The new shape must be in the same family as the original shape (triangles and triangles or rectangles and rectangles).
- The original and the new version must have the same angle sizes.
- All sides must share in the same numerical relationship. In other words, what you do to one side (e.g., enlarge three times or cut in half), you must do to the other sides.

The flyer looks wrong because the width was barely enlarged, but the length was enlarged two times.

Perimeter may be a new idea for some students. Introduce the term and demonstrate finding perimeter. Ask:

> **What does it mean to find the perimeter of a shape?**

> **How can we find perimeter?**

State that perimeter refers to the sum of the length of the sides, or the distance around a shape. Then demonstrate the following ways:

- Trace the edges of the rectangle.
- Measure and add the lengths of the sides.

Add new words to the class vocabulary list.

Activity: Giant-Size

Set the scene by describing the task: to make larger-than-life objects. You could refer to a story like "Jack and the Beanstalk" or *Gulliver's Travels*, where there are giant-size people and objects.

Group students and distribute the objects. Students are to fill in the chart *Activity: Giant-Size* (*Student Book*, p. 42). The chart in the *Student Book* has an extra column, not included on the class newsprint, to help students keep track of their steps.

Heads Up!

Set a ground rule for measuring: Everyone should round up or down to the nearest whole centimeter.

Let students know where they can check their work when they are ready. They should correct their work but leave their original answers as well so you can see where problems occurred. Ask them to revisit any discrepancies and then to post their measurements on the class newsprint.

The emphasis in the summary is on the concepts of perimeter and similarity, not on correcting mistakes that arise from addition or multiplication errors. However, since miscalculations can lead to confusion, make sure the correct measurements are posted.

Summary Discussion

Students post their enlarged shapes near the originals. Invite them to check each other's work, and discuss the work as a group.

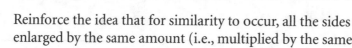

 How do you know the shapes are similar?

 Which aspects of the shapes are exactly alike? Which aspects look similar? Which look different?

 Do the angle measurements double when the sides are doubled? Why?

Reinforce the idea that for similarity to occur, all the sides of the shape have to be enlarged by the same amount (i.e., multiplied by the same number). Ask students to comment on each other's new shapes and data.

💬 **How do the original and new versions compare?**

Model or give sentence starters to help students practice new vocabulary and concepts. For example:

💬 **The new shape is three times longer than the original. It is three times wider. The perimeter is three times longer.**

Direct attention to the sides of the shape by tracing the outside edges and asking:

💬 **What do you call this?**

💬 **What did you have to measure to find perimeter?**

💬 **What operation did you use: multiplication, division, addition, or subtraction? How? What shortcuts did you use?**

Review conventions for labeling: *w*, *l*, cm.

Heads Up!

Do not push for the perimeter formula at this point. That will emerge in later lessons.

This discussion lays the groundwork for contrasting area with perimeter. If class time runs out before students fully grasp the concept of perimeter, plan to spend more time on *Lesson 5*, where it will be brought up again and contrasted with area.

Students write in *Reflections, Student Book*, p. 154, what they want to remember about similar shapes. They could play with the idea of similarity by thinking about questions such as:

💬 **How tall would you be if this new scarf fit you the way the original fits you? How could you find out?**

◎ Practice

Brainstorm a list of all the concepts covered in the lessons so far. Advise students to review their practice sheets and vocabulary. *Interim Assessment 1* focuses on attributes of shapes and angle measurements. Share ideas for how to prepare for the test, e.g., by making a list of what you have learned and reviewing shape names.

2 Times, 5 Times, 10 Times, p. 43
For practice finding dimensions of enlarged shapes.

Similar? True or False? p. 44

Perimeter Problems, p. 47

Similar or Not? p. 48
For practice identifying similar shapes.

 Test Practice

Test Practice, p. 57

Looking Closely

Observe whether students are able to

Identify width and length as dimensions

Do students have difficulty accepting that the terms length and width are somewhat arbitrarily applied? They may press you for a right answer. Width is usually horizontal and is usually the shorter dimension. Build consensus on the use of the terms.

Use a ruler or a meter stick marked in centimeters to measure width and length

Do students know to start measuring from the mark for zero, not one? Unless your students are comfortable with decimals in measurement, make sure to round measurements to the nearest centimeter.

Identify similar shapes using spatial comparisons and dimension measurements

Do students discount some shapes as similar? Often people believe that shapes' orientation determines similarity. Look for students whose understanding of similarity is shaky. Give them a chance to rotate shapes and trace corresponding sides and angles and measure them. You can direct attention to this issue during the summary by rotating the original or enlarged shape.

To check that originals and enlargements are similar, students can directly compare angles by fitting the original onto the enlargement. To verify that the length and width of the enlarged version are similar to those of the original, they can flip the original item over and over along each dimension, counting the number of times in each direction.

Find perimeter by adding the lengths of the sides

Lay the groundwork for shortcuts to find perimeter. Begin by calling on students who realize that they do not need to measure every side of a shape; ask them to explain their reasoning. Ask students who are measuring every side what their steps are. Encourage them to list both width measurements, then both length measurements. This prepares them for understanding the multiplication in the perimeter formula for a rectangle.

WHAT TO LOOK FOR IN *LESSON 4*	WHO STANDS OUT? (LIST STUDENTS' INITIALS)			NOTES FOR NEXT STEPS
	STRONG	ADEQUATE	NEEDS WORK	
Concept Development • Identifies length and width in a rectangle • Uses dimension measurements to compare shapes and identify similar shapes • Uses spatial comparisons to identify similar shapes • Finds perimeter by adding lengths of sides • Finds perimeter using shortcuts				
Expressive Capacity • Articulates reasons why two shapes are or are not similar • Explains similarity using dimension comparisons				
Use of Tools • Uses a ruler to measure width and length to the nearest centimeter				
Background Knowledge • Uses an informal definition of similarity and adds a mathematical meaning to the working definition				

Rationale

By constructing similar shapes, students have the opportunity to isolate two main geometric ideas: perimeter and similarity. The notion of similarity allows for generalizing from one shape to the next; it enables a person to figure out missing values in one shape based on known values in another. This lesson lays the groundwork for scale by focusing on the importance of all sides maintaining consistent relationships.

Students often confuse area and perimeter. Taking shapes off the page and into outline form highlights their edges. Practice with measuring sides of shapes is meant to instill a connection between edges and perimeter, whereas area and surface will be connected in *Lesson 5*.

Math Background

Shapes are similar when corresponding angles are equal and corresponding sides are proportional. The emphasis in the lesson stays on enlarging all sides by the same factor. Enlarging and reducing are associated with multiplication and division; a tip-off to this is found in the language we use—*factor*.

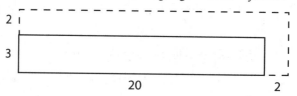

Students might wonder why you cannot produce a similar shape by adding the same amount to all sides. If you add 2 inches to a side of 3 inches, you have added more than half the original length. If you add 2 to a side of 20, you have added only a tenth of the original length. Adding could change the proportionality, whereas multiplication preserves it.

In similar shapes, the length, width, and perimeter all increase or decrease by the same factor. However, the area does not. Think about a rectangle enlarged 200% on a copying machine. The length, width, and perimeter will double, but the area will quadruple. *Lesson 7* presents a situation like this.

Test situations often present similar shapes in different orientations (see below). Encourage everyone to turn and manipulate figures and shapes,

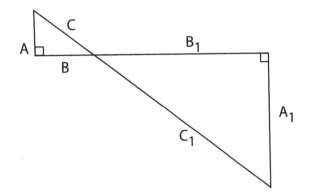

Facilitation

Making the Lesson Easier

If students are having a hard time articulating what is wrong with the flyer in the *Opening Discussion*, give them the business card and flyer to manipulate. They might want to use tools to measure the two, or they can use the original business card as a unit of measure by physically comparing it to the flyer.

Making the Lesson Harder

Here are three suggestions for making the activity more difficult:

- The larger the factor for enlarging, the more challenging the math and the construction. Make the factor 12, for example.

- Three-sided and oddly shaped, four-sided figures will present a different challenge. Students may need some help getting the angles right. They can use their angle demonstrators to outline the angle in the original and then trace that angle to establish the corners of their enlarged shape.

- Enlarging is likely to be easier than scaling down, as multiplication tends to be easier for students than dividing. As a challenge, ask students to make a new shape one-half, one-third, or one-fourth of the original size.

Focusing on similarity requires attention to various aspects of shapes.

When Marilyn, the teacher, asked students about her flyer and business card, students responded as follows:

Student: "Both are rectangles."

Student: "They have right angles."

Teacher: "So they are similar?"

Students answered in the affirmative, and the teacher realized they were using a generic definition for "similar," not a mathematical one. Marilyn said, "I am not going to pay for this. It is not right."

One student then asked to see the larger version folded in half.

Student: "You wanted it enlarged up and down, not just across."

Student: "Enlarge both length and width."

Teacher: "So if I asked them to double it, they should double all the dimensions."

Students in pairs constructed enlarged outlines of their objects. Most pairs had a rectangular or square object. Fingers were flying in these groups as they measured, calculated, cut, and taped ribbon to outline the new shapes and display them on newsprint. One pair, however, had a triangular pennant.

When the teacher and I checked in with the Duke University pennant pair, they had drawn a line for the base of the triangle. Doubled, it measured 44 cm. The sides of the original were 63 cm, and they knew the next line they had to draw would be 126 cm. However, they looked a bit stuck. They wondered whether they should measure the original angle with a protractor, until Marilyn suggested they use an angle demonstrator. She modeled holding it against the original angle, and students traced the angle from the angle demonstrator onto their newsprint. They extended the lines from the angles to form two sides and the third angle.

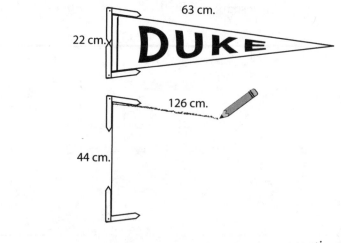

continued on next page

continued from previous page

In the *Summary Discussion*, everyone's enlarged and original versions were posted at the front of the room.

Marilyn asked of one group, "What happened to the perimeter?"

Students recognized that when the shape was enlarged by a factor of two or four, the perimeter increased by the same factor.

Teacher: "One last thing: What is the definition for similar?"

Student: "Double."

Teacher: "Always?"

Student: "Smaller or bigger."

Student: "Same shape. Different sides."

Student: "Oh! Same shape. Same angles. Different sides."

Marilyn Moses, observed by Martha Merson
Brockton Adult Learning Center, Brockton, MA

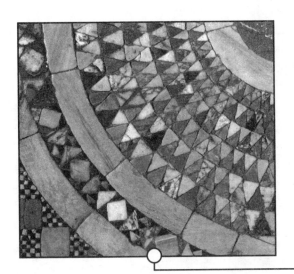

Facilitating Interim Assessment 1: Shapes and Angles

> *Which shapes are familiar?*

Synopsis

This is a chance to consolidate the concepts covered in *Lessons 1–4*. Giving a quiz can provide feedback students take seriously.

1. Students work independently on a written assessment on the attributes and angles of shapes.
2. Teacher works one-to-one with students on an oral section.

Objectives

- Display knowledge of shape names and attributes
- Identify angles and perimeter

Materials/Prep

- Copies of the quiz

Assessment Activity

There are four sections. Use one or more depending on your group. The student book includes all but the third part where you pose questions aloud.

1. Choose a Shape.
Give each student a shape, either a triangle or rectangle, and a blank piece of paper. Have crayons or markers on the table and rulers marked in centimeters. Students describe the attributes of the shape.

2. Spot the Shapes.
Students look at the picture of a house. They circle and label any shapes from the list that they see. If students have access to digital or Polaroid™ cameras, they can take a walk and snap the pictures instead of using the ones in their books.

3. Show Off What You Know.
The following list of "show me" prompts lends itself to individual meetings with students. You could ask each student to pick two or three from both lists or read off a couple of your choice.

Angles

- A right angle with your feet
- A 45° angle with your feet
- A 30° angle with the door
- A 180° degree angle in the room
- An angle larger than 90° with two pens or pencils
- An angle smaller than 30° with two pens or pencils
- A scissor opening less than 45°
- The angle at which he or she would position a cookbook holder or music stand for comfortable reading

Sides

- The perimeter of an imaginary rectangle
- The area of an imaginary triangle
- The perimeter of an imaginary triangle
- The perimeter of an imaginary hexagon
- The perimeter of the door
- The perimeter of a book cover
- The perimeter of a pocket

4. Applying Ideas from Geometry
Students solve up to three problems with real-world contexts.

Summary Discussion

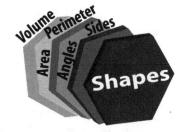

Ask students to discuss the assessment, focusing on their reactions.

What did you find you can do now that you could not do before you started the unit?

What was hard? What was easy?

If students thought the assessment was difficult or if they felt unprepared, ask:

How might you have prepared differently?

It is often helpful to ask students whether they felt they knew material that was not addressed by the assessment. This helps you determine which concepts they thought were important and gives you feedback on where you might want to shift the teaching emphasis.

WHAT TO LOOK FOR IN MIDPOINT ASSESSMENT 1: SHAPES AND ANGLES	WHO STANDS OUT? (LIST STUDENTS' INITIALS)			NOTES FOR NEXT STEPS
	STRONG	ADEQUATE	NEEDS WORK	
Concept Development • Associates shape with name • Isolates shapes within a landscape • Identifies right angles • Estimates angle size • Finds perimeter • Identifies perimeter as outside edge • Measures sides accurately • Applies perimeter to cost situation				
Expressive Capacity • Describes angles • Shows steps for problem solving				
Use of Tools • Measures to the nearest centimeter				

Line Up By Size

How do the sizes compare?

Synopsis

In previous lessons, students compared and measured shapes' angles, sides, and perimeters. This is the first of three lessons in which students use perimeter *and* area to describe shapes.

1. The teacher models three methods to compare areas.

2. Students use at least two methods to compare and order six basic shapes according to the size of their areas.

3. The class reviews the area comparisons.

4. The whole class or small groups compare the same shapes' perimeter measurements, determining that shapes with equal surface area will not necessarily have a perimeter of equal length.

Objectives

- Compare areas visually and physically
- Distinguish between area and perimeter

Materials/Prep

- Centimeter rulers
- Colored paper
- Newsprint with a copy of the chart from *Student Book*, p. 55
- Scissors
- Shape Set, one envelope per student pair or group (*Blackline Masters 2* and *3*)

- Student work from *Lesson 4*
- Two different shoes, one a little longer and thinner than the other

Opening Discussion

Pose a scenario that will open a discussion of multiple ways to measure two-dimensional (2-D) surfaces. Ask:

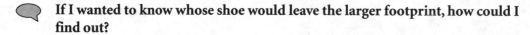 **If I wanted to know whose shoe would leave the larger footprint, how could I find out?**

List students' answers and post them where students can refer to them later. Model or have students demonstrate at least three ways to compare the size of the shoes. Hold the shoes up sole to sole; "eyeball" them; make footprints (trace each one on a piece of different colored paper), cut them out, and place one on top of the other.

Referring to the shapes students made in *Lesson 4*, ask:

When we enlarged shapes, we looked at edges. How is that different from what we just looked at to compare footprints?

Introduce the term "**area**."

- Note that the comparison goes beyond length, width, and the edges to the surface of the shape.
- Make a sweeping gesture over the sole of one of the shoes.
- Show the notation of "sq. units" and the exponent, but do not belabor the notation discussion at this point.

Add "area" to the class vocabulary sheet. Ask students:

What are some situations where you compare or estimate size?

When you picture the situation, what is being compared—area, perimeter, length, or width?

Have a few examples in mind to jumpstart a list, such as comparing waistlines or leg lengths on pants, or figuring out whether the space on a countertop is big enough for a microwave.

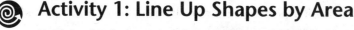 Activity 1: Line Up Shapes by Area

Explain the first part of the activity: establishing the order for shapes according to area. See directions for *Line Up Shapes by Area* (*Student Book*, p. 55). Students will look at the shapes quickly, compare their estimates with those of their partners, and check actual measurements by *physically* comparing the shapes.

Students work in pairs or groups for 10–15 minutes. Distribute an envelope with one Shape Set (*Blackline Masters 2* and *3*) to each group, and ask students to work with Shapes 1–6. There is one correct order, although there are different ways to reach the right answer.

Heads Up!

The actual order, by area, of the six shapes is 2, 1 = 5 = 6, 3 = 4.

By Area (from smallest to largest)

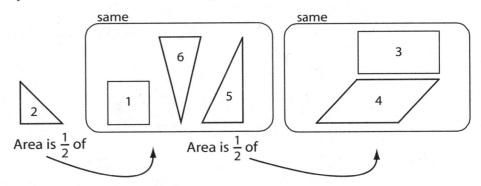

When students have finished ordering the shapes by area, post the correct order and say:

💬 **This is what I have in my teacher book. Does it seem right to everyone?**

As a whole class, discuss what students found.

💬 **How is the order the same or different from what you expected?**

💬 **You tried different methods to find the area. Which one do you trust and why?**

💬 **What is the relationship among the shapes?**

💬 **How can you explain the fact that Shape 3 (the rectangle) and Shape 4 (the parallelogram) have the same area?**

💬 **Make a statement comparing areas that uses the words "double" or "half."**

🌀 Activity 2: Line Up Shapes by Perimeter

Launch the second part of the activity by asking:

💬 **In general, if you compared two shapes by area and knew which one was bigger, would its perimeter also be bigger?**

💬 **What do you predict for the order of the shapes according to perimeter (same as the order by area or not)?**

💬 **How could we check it out?**

If necessary, quickly review the idea of measuring the edges, and contrast this with the methods for finding area. Students should measure in centimeters.

Heads Up!

The actual order by perimeter is 2, 1, 6, 5, 3, and 4.

By Perimeter (from smallest to largest)

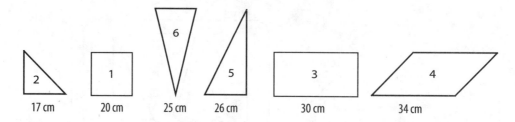

2	1	6	5	3	4
17 cm	20 cm	25 cm	26 cm	30 cm	34 cm

Have students compare orders by perimeter to reach consensus. Then have them compare the agreed-on order by perimeter with the order of shapes from smallest to largest by area. Ask:

💬 **What do you notice looking at the two orders—by perimeter and by area?**

💬 **Did this surprise you? Why?**

Summary Discussion

The main ideas for students to grasp are an understanding of area as surface and an understanding of perimeter as a measure independent from area. Ask:

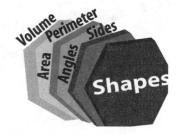

💬 **What were the ways we compared shapes?**

💬 **How was looking at perimeter different from looking at area?**

End with a conversation about the usefulness of different ways to measure shapes.

💬 **Which do *you* expect to use most frequently: dimensions (length and width), perimeter, area, or angle measurements? Why? Provide at least one example to support your opinion.**

Students record their thoughts in *Reflections* (*Student Book*, p. 154).

Practice

Seeing Perimeter and Area, p. 56
For practice distinguishing between area and perimeter situations.

The Job Demands..., p. 57
For practice distinguishing between area, perimeter, and dimensions (length and width).

The Caterers' Question, p. 58
For practice with the concept of area conservation and changing perimeters.

 Extension

Area and Perimeter in My Neighborhood, p. 59
Students find their own examples of area and perimeter.

 Test Practice

Test Practice, p. 60

Looking Closely

Observe whether students are able to

Compare areas visually and physically

If students are not manipulating the shapes, model overlapping, tracing, and cutting them and moving parts of the shapes around; encourage students to do the same. Prompt for numerical statements comparing areas using "double" and "half."

Distinguish between area and perimeter

The difference between area and perimeter measures is not always clear to students. One teacher reported, "We talked about the difference between area and perimeter. Just when the students would repeat back to me what the difference was, someone would get confused, and then everyone would start getting confused."

If students in your class do not understand the difference between area and perimeter, pull out their work from the last class, where they found the sum of the sides of shapes. Call on students to see whether they remember what was measured in *Lesson 4* (edges) compared to what was measured in *Activity 1* of this lesson (areas). Hand movements (tracing the edges and sweeping across the area) help some students visualize and internalize the concepts. Use the classroom as a source for shapes. Trace the edges of a shape or make a sweeping gesture, and ask, "Does this remind you of area or perimeter?"

Making connections to real-life situations also may be effective. Ask students to think about the difference between the picture and its frame; the size of a garden versus the fence around it; or the carpet on a floor versus the floorboard trim around the room.

Students will notice that the area and perimeter orders are different. They will encounter this concept of conservation of space in *The Caterers' Question* (*Student Book*, p. 58), and again in *Lesson 6: Combining Rectangles.*

WHAT TO LOOK FOR IN *LESSON 5*	WHO STANDS OUT? (LIST STUDENTS' INITIALS)			NOTES FOR NEXT STEPS
	STRONG	ADEQUATE	NEEDS WORK	
Concept Development • Demonstrates understanding of area by comparing the surfaces of shapes • Demonstrates understanding of perimeter by physically comparing lengths of shapes' sides • Finds area by comparing shapes directly				
Expressive Capacity • Articulates reasons why one shape has a larger area than another • Articulates reasons why one shape has a larger perimeter than another • Explains what distinguishes area from perimeter • Explains one strategy for finding area and perimeter • Describes comparisons using "double" and "half"				
Use of Tools • Manipulates shapes, rotating them and sliding them for comparisons • Uses shapes to compare lengths, widths, and area • Measures lengths appropriately				
Background Knowledge • Gives examples of area and perimeter from prior experiences				

Rationale

Space and size are advertising obsessions in the United States, where the predominant cultural values are reflected in the statement "bigger is better." The size of two-dimensional shapes can be described by two common measurements: area (amount of surface) and perimeter (length of the bounding edge). Students who confuse these measurements can benefit from an investigation that juxtaposes the two and highlights their visible differences. The mathematics explored here lays the groundwork for making comparisons using various methods.

Facilitation

Encourage students to cut the extra shapes as a way of seeing the relationship between two different shapes. To prevent losing and confusing the parts, suggest labeling each part with the shape number or coloring each shape a different color before cutting them apart.

Area/Perimeter Relationships

When you guide students to consider why Shapes 1, 5, and 6 have the same area but different perimeters, focus on what happens to the sides of the shapes. For instance, the rectangle has two sides that are longer and two sides that are shorter than the sides of the square. The space has been rearranged, not eliminated or increased. Let them explore the idea by actually cutting the rectangle apart to fit into the square.

Making the Lesson Easier

Have the groups start by comparing the areas of Shapes 1, 2, and 3. Then add Shapes 4, 5, and 6.

One teacher reported on her students' responses to the question of footprint size.

I felt the opening discussion about footprints worked very well. I started the discussion by finding a student who had on a pair of shoes that I thought were about the same size as mine but had a different look. My shoes were a little boxy, and I found a student that had on pointy shoes. Vera joined me at the front of the room so every one could see.

Teacher: "Vera and I are going to take a walk on the beach…with our shoes on. Who do you think has the larger footprint?"

Student: "Yours; it is bigger."

Student: "But Vera's is longer."

Student: "But yours is wider."

Teacher: "What could we do?"

Student: "Measure."

Teacher: "Oh. What would you measure?"

Student: "Length."

Teacher: "Just length?"

Student: "Maybe width."

Teacher: "That makes me think you are measuring a rectangle."

Student: "Well, your shoes look like a rectangle, but Vera's look more like a triangle."

Student: "Do you want perimeter?"

Teacher: "I want to know which is larger. Is that how you see it?"

Student: "No. I think I want to know which footprint has the largest surface."

Teacher: "How could we show that?"

Fiona suggested we place our shoes together.

Eduardo suggested we trace our footprints. I asked him to come up. Vera and I each stepped on a piece of paper, and Eduardo traced our footprints.

Ella suggested that we could cut out the footprints and compare them. We did. We were able to see that if some of the "point" was cut off of Vera's shoe, it could fill in part of my rectangular-shaped footprint. What we saw was that both footprints were about the same size but very different looking.

Teacher: So, we looked at the surface to determine which is larger. What do you call that?

continued on next page

continued from previous page

Student: "Is that area?"

Teacher: "It is!"

Marilyn Moses
Brockton Adult Learning Center, Brockton, MA

Students thought all the shapes had to have different areas because they had different shapes.

I put this question on the board: Can two shapes have different perimeters but the same area? (yes or no). Though they all got the answer correct (yes), they had a lot of difficulty explaining it. We spent time writing and revising until we had good arguments on paper.

Jonna Rao
SafeSpace, New York City, NY

A dissenting voice prompts deeper mathematical conversation.

I set the task of finding what order the shapes had by area. I was surprised that a student who often requires longer processing time was the one to question the first class ordering and to instigate a more rigorous examination of Triangles 5 and 6. My teen student established the order of Shapes 3 and 4 and ably defended his choice.

Roberta Froelich
Middlesex Community College, Bedford, MA

Combining Rectangles

How much area does the hopscotch game take?

Synopsis

Students continue to explore area and perimeter of basic shapes, working with centimeter grid paper.

1. Students make and measure a composite shape made of rectangles.

2. They compare total areas and total perimeters of the individual rectangles and the composite shape.

3. Through a review of the investigation, students generalize that area is conserved in the new shape, but perimeter is not.

Objectives

- Calculate area of a rectangle using square centimeters
- Articulate what happens to area and perimeter when rectangles are combined
- Find the area of any shape composed of multiple rectangles

Materials/Prep

- Centimeter grid paper (*Blackline Master 29*)
- Centimeter rulers
- Markers and highlighters
- Tape or glue stick

Prepare overhead or enlarged version of the square on *Blackline Master 13*.

Prepare newsprint as follows:

Shape Name & Sketch	Areas of four rectangles (sq. cm)				Sum of Areas (sq. cm)	Area of Composite
Elisa's Cake	50	20	8	16	94	94 sq. cm
Generalization:						

Shape Name & Sketch	Perimeters of four rectangles (cm)				Sum of Perimeters (cm)	Perimeter of Composite
Elisa's Cake	30	24	12	20	86	50 cm
Generalization:						

Opening Discussion

Refer to the last lesson by reminding students that they compared the areas of different shapes. Note that finding the areas of shapes that are rectangular is easier than finding the areas of other shapes, but the problems in life and on tests are rarely so straightforward.

Review definitions for perimeter and area and the ways to find them. If it was assigned, go over *See ing Perimeter and Area* (*Student Book*, p. 56), or do it together as a warm-up if you think students could use the review.

Introduce the idea of square units by showing the 5 x 5 square on centimeter grid paper.

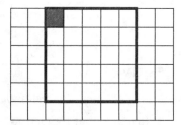

Shade in one square and say:

> **This is one square centimeter. How many of these square centimeters cover the surface of the square?**

Color in the squares as students count, reinforcing the idea of area as surface.

> **What are other ways to find the total number of square centimeters?**

Record students' strategies as they share them, for example, counting by twos or fives, multiplying rows by columns, or adding repeatedly.

Highlight notation in one or more ways.

- Write the words on the transparency or the board (25 square centimeters; 25 sq. cm; 25 cm²). Draw a line 25 cm long. Do students see the difference between 25 sq. cm and 25 cm? Do they acknowledge that writing "25" without saying whether the number refers to square centimeters or centimeters would be misleading?

- Note that the standard measurement for area is squares, not circles or hexagons.

- Ask everyone to make sure area is reported in square centimeters (sq. cm) and perimeter in centimeters (cm).

Heads Up!

Refrain at this point from teaching the formulas for perimeter and area of a rectangle. Allow students to figure area and perimeter out with the grid paper. This lesson will provide experiences that form a basis for understanding the formulas in *Lesson 7*.

 ## Activity 1: Drawing Four Rectangles

Direct students to *Activity 1: Drawing Four Rectangles* (*Student Book*, p. 62). Distribute cm grid paper. All students draw four rectangles and find and record their dimensions, areas, and perimeters. When students finish, they should have a classmate check their work.

Before moving on, discuss ways to count and keep track of the number of squares. Ask:

What do you think will happen to the area if you combine these four shapes into a new shape?

What do you think will happen to the perimeter?

Write down your predictions on p. 62, and complete *Activity 2: Making a Composite Shape* to find out whether you are right.

 ## Activity 2: Making a Composite Shape

Students create their composite shapes. Once they have completed their charts (figured out area, perimeter, number of angles, and number of sides and recorded this information), ask them to exchange shapes and data with each other to verify calculations.

Ask students to post their composite shapes and findings on the newsprint sheets. They need information from both activity pages (pp. 62 and 63) to do this. If some finish earlier than others, assign *Extension: Sides and Angles* (*Student Book*, p. 68).

Ask students to talk about how they calculated area. Choose two or three students whom you observed using multiplication or repeated addition to share how they determined area of their shapes. Point out the relationship between repeated addition and multiplication.

Summary Discussion

Discussion should focus on the data the students posted. If students have trouble grasping all of the generalizations, focus on one and its implications.

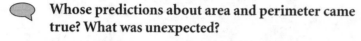

💬 **Whose predictions about area and perimeter came true? What was unexpected?**

Probe for reasons underlying accurate and inaccurate predictions. Draw attention to students' data on area.

💬 **Looking at your data, what do you notice about the areas of the individual rectangles compared with the area of the composite shape?**

Write students' statements on the board under "Generalizations."

Draw one or two multi-rectangular shapes and ask:

💬 **How would I find the area for something like this?**

Make sure everyone understands that breaking the shape down into rectangles, finding the area for each, and adding the areas will yield a total. Or they can add lines to contain both rectangles, calculate the size of the new rectangle and of the additional "empty" space, then subtract the latter from the former.

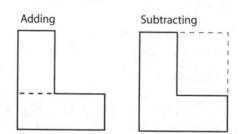

Now review the perimeter data. Ask:

💬 **How does your method for finding area compare with your method for finding perimeter?**

💬 **What do you notice about the perimeters of the individual rectangles compared with the perimeter of the composite shape?**

Post students' comments under "Generalizations." Ask:

💬 **Why would the perimeter of the composite shape be a smaller number than the one for the perimeters of the four rectangles added together?**

💬 **Will this always be true? Why?**

Ask students to give examples and demonstrations, for example, pushing together tables so everyone can see that the surface does not change, but the number of exposed edges is quite different.

Students record their thoughts in *Reflections* (*Student Book*, p. 154): "What do you want to remember about area and perimeter? How will you find the area of shapes that look like combined rectangles?"

- Perimeter is sides or the outside of any shape, finding the perimeter you meaure the outside with Cm.

- Area is the surface of any shape or inside of a shape to find the area you use 'Sq. Cm'

Practice

Area of 24 Sq. Cm, p. 64
For practice comparing area and perimeter.

Divide the Shapes, p. 65
For practice sectioning off rectangles, the first step to finding the area of composite shapes.

Cookie Cutter, p. 66
For practice creating a shape and applying perimeter and area to a context with implications for cost.

Area in Packaging, p. 67
For practice finding area using a cardboard box.

Extension

Sides and Angles, p. 68
For practice generalizing about characteristics of composite shapes.

Test Practice

Test Practice, p. 69

 **Looking Closely**

Observe whether students are able to

Calculate area of a rectangle using square centimeters

How do students find area—by counting, skip counting, or multiplying? Ask students who are counting one by one whether they could also count by a larger number, for instance, two or five. The students' work will indicate their strategies, as in the examples provided. Counting one by one may feel like the most conscientious way to some students. These students need practice to become fluid with a more efficient approach. For those who are skip counting, ask whether there is a quicker way to find the number of square centimeters in, for instance, five rows of four squares.

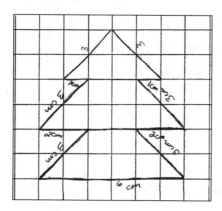

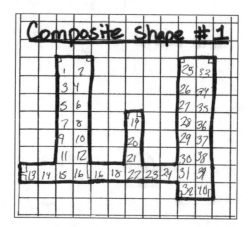

Articulate what happens to area and perimeter when rectangles are combined

Perimeter changes are hard to explain. One way to see this is to highlight the perimeter of all the original rectangles in one color and then highlight the new shape's perimeter with another color. Ask what happened to the original perimeters when the shapes were combined. Do students notice that some have disappeared? Offer a real-life example, such as putting up fencing. Four separate plots require more fencing than combining the plots. Why?

Find the area of any shape composed of multiple rectangles

Do students understand area well enough to see the new shape made up of all the different areas combined? Suggest students do *Extension: Sides and Angles* (*Student Book*, p. 68), where they combine rectangles and record area and perimeter data for them.

WHAT TO LOOK FOR IN LESSON 6	WHO STANDS OUT? (LIST STUDENTS' INITIALS)			NOTES FOR NEXT STEPS
	STRONG	ADEQUATE	NEEDS WORK	
Concept Development • Finds area of rectangle using square centimeters • Combines rectangles to form composite shape • Finds area of composite shape • Finds perimeter of composite shape • Makes generalization about area and perimeter of composite shapes				
Expressive Capacity • Distinguishes between area and perimeter of rectangle • Distinguishes between area and perimeter of composite shape • Articulates what has happened to the sides when the rectangles are merged to form composite shape • Writes generalized statements about area and perimeter of composite shapes				
Use of Tools • Uses sq. cm paper to draw rectangles • Cuts and tapes together rectangles				
Background Knowledge • Refers to formulas of rectangle area and perimeter • Relates composite shapes to familiar objects				

Rationale

By combining rectangles, comparing their areas and perimeters, noting relationships, and articulating generalizations, students acquire a fundamental understanding of the differences between area and perimeter.

Math Background

The difference between area and perimeter of rectangles and composite shapes formed by those rectangles is that the inside surface amount remains the same—there is no overlap in the shapes that are merely set side by side—but the outside bounds of the sides are different. So, although area is conserved, perimeter is not. The same would be true if the shapes were triangles, hexagons, or other polygons: The area of the composite shape is the sum of the areas of the individual shapes, but the perimeter of the composite shape is *not* the sum of the perimeters of the individual shapes. Understanding the definitions for area and perimeter helps explain these differences.

The number of angles in a rectangle is four, and they are all right angles (90°). When two identical rectangles are set side by side or stacked, the resulting composite shape has four sides and four angles, not eight. The area of the resulting composite shape is the sum of the areas of each rectangle, and the perimeter is smaller than the sum of the perimeters of the two rectangles.

When two different-size rectangles are composed, they may or may not share a complete side. If they look like this, for example,

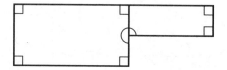

the area of the composite is the sum of the individual areas, but the perimeter is slightly smaller. Examining the angles, we find there are five right angles and one other 270° angle. Note that the composite shape has six sides.

Facilitation

Making the Lesson Easier

One field-test teacher reported how she helped her students who struggled to find the perimeter, number of angles, and sides. Her strategy made the task easier for students.

> When my students cut out the shapes and taped them together, none seemed able to count the areas or perimeters correctly the first time around. They were skipping sides with the perimeters, skipping squares with the areas, and seemed at a loss for identifying corners and sides. I had to go around to each person (because they were working at different paces) and ask questions to help him or her think through the answers. For example, if someone said her shape had 6 sides when it had 12, I would say, "Okay, show me the sides." As she identified each side, I would trace it with a highlighter. When she reached the sixth, I would say, "Do you see any more sides we missed?" Most students understood.

Making the Lesson Harder

A third generalization can be made based on a count of angles and sides. When students agree that the number of sides and the number of angles in a composite shape are the same, post that generalization. This insight might lead students to check shapes such as the octagon or hexagon to see whether the rule proves true for other shapes.

The area and perimeter findings can be expressed using algebraic notation. Tell students that mathematicians often record their generalizations in shorthand, using letters to stand for certain measurements.

Model this by saying the generalization for area aloud and writing it in shorthand, with A_c meaning the area of the composite shape and A_1, A_2, A_3, and A_4 standing for the areas of each of the four rectangles. Connect the algebraic equation to people's natural language.

$$A_c = A_1 + A_2 + A_3 + A_4$$

(The area of the big one) (is the same as) (the four areas put together),

or the area of the composite shape equals the sum of the areas of the rectangles.

Check the algebraic statement with test cases: Plug in numbers from the class's newsprint.

Write:

$$P_c \qquad P_1 + P_2 + P_3 + P_4$$

Ask students to complete the statement using an appropriate symbol. Symbols such as greater than ($>$), less than ($<$), or the symbol for inequality ($\neq$) can make the statement true. This rule should also be true for every case. You could pose a challenge to students to come up with a design for which the rule would not be true.

Multiple experiences with area and perimeter can help students build confidence and intuition.

What I have noticed at this point is that my students have seen a relationship between length and width and perimeter; they are starting to double each and add them together. They have not noticed that they could measure length and width on the graph paper without a ruler. They see no relationship yet between length and width and area. One student was counting by ones and another student showed her how she was counting the rows by fives and twos.

I thought the student that counted by ones was having a major breakthrough; when asked to predict the area of the composite shape, the first thing she said was, "That's easy—it's just the area of all the shapes added together." But instead of adding the areas from the first page together, she started re-counting the entire area by ones. She also had problems on the first page because she did not draw her rectangles on the lines. Checking each other's work was great because her partner could point out her mistake. It is so much less intimidating to students who are not very comfortable with math for a student to point out their errors than for the teacher to point them out.

Phyllis Flanagan
Rock Valley Community College, Rockford, IL

Disappearing Grid Lines

> *What is the missing information?*

Synopsis

Students articulate the formulas for area and perimeter of rectangles.

1. Students find missing data about dimensions, area, and/or perimeter values for various rectangles, using square-centimeter grid paper as a tool.

2. Students find missing dimensions for rectangles without the support of a grid.

3. Students post their findings from these two exercises and explain the relationship between the dimensions of a rectangle and its area and perimeter.

4. Students explore the areas of right triangles and explain their relationships to the areas of rectangles.

Objectives

- Find missing dimensions, areas, and perimeters of rectangles
- Record the formula for area and perimeter
- Extend what is known about calculating the area of a rectangle to calculating the area of a right triangle

Materials/Prep

- Scissors

Make a copy of the charts "Missing Measurements" and "When the Grid Lines Disappear" (*Student Book*, p. 72 and 73) on either newsprint or a transparency.

Copy right triangles on *Blackline Master 14*, one set per pair of students.

Opening Discussion

Remind students of the work done in *Lesson 6*, where they drew their own rectangles and calculated area and perimeter for rectangles and composite shapes. Explain that today they will find area and perimeter of rectangles someone else has designed. They will use what they know to find missing information.

Activity 1: Missing Measurements

Refer students to *Activity 1: Missing Measurements* (*Student Book*, p. 72). Students work independently and then check results with a partner. Volunteers post answers on the chart you prepared.

Draw the group together to review any problems that caused disagreement. Then ask:

💬 **How can you verify your answers?**

💬 **Did anyone see the problem differently?**

Activity 2: When the Grid Lines Disappear

Transition to finding area without the support of a grid by asking:

💬 **The strategies you suggested work well if you can see the square centimeters, but what happens when the paper has no squares?**

Model finding the area when there is no grid in two ways. Show a 3 cm × 4 cm rectangle with tick marks indicating the units.

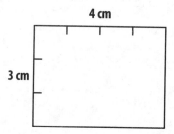

Ask students:

💬 **How would you find the area of a rectangle like this?**

As students share their methods, ask volunteers to demonstrate or restate what is said. Find the area of a few more rectangles together for additional practice.

Next draw a rectangle with no tick marks, but with dimensions labeled.

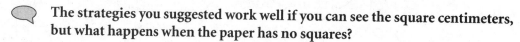

Ask students:

💬 **How would you find the area of a rectangle like this?**

💬 **How could you check your answer?**

Students find the missing data for the rectangles in *When the Grid Lines Disappear* (*Student Book*, p. 73).

As they finish, students fill in the answers on the chart you posted. Agree on the correct answers. Then ask students to demonstrate the strategies they used. Refer to grid-paper models if anyone is uncertain.

Indicating the answers recorded on both charts, ask:

💬 **What did you notice when you looked at the length, width, and area entries?** (Highlight these in some way.)

💬 **Is this true for every case?**

💬 **What did you notice when you looked at the entries for the dimensions and the perimeter entry?** (Be aware that this relationship is not as clear-cut as the area relationship.)

💬 **Is this true for every case?**

Words and Equations

Record students' words as they express the rule for finding area. Question any incorrect statements, such as "You can multiply all the sides to get the area."

Then translate the statements into a formula using algebraic notation. For example, if a student says, "To find the area, you multiply the length by the width," write: "$A = lw$."

Share the different ways of writing the formula symbolically. Use the different symbols for multiplication, and rewrite the equation to find l or w using various symbols for division. Conclude with the form most often used: $A = lw$. Double-check students' understanding by writing the letters in a different order: $l \times w = A$ or $A = wl$. Ask:

💬 **How are these the same?**

Next record students' rules for finding perimeter. Have students test their own statements by giving examples. Again connect students' language with the algebraic notation. For example, "You add the length plus the width and do that again to get the perimeter" might translate as "$(l + w) + (l + w) = P$."

Take time to connect the various systems of notation for finding perimeter. For instance, explore the connection between $2(l) + 2(w) = (l + w) + (l + w)$ and the more general $2(l + w) = P$.

If your students are preparing for a standardized test, share some sample questions from that test that employ this notation. Or if the test (like the GED test) has a formula sheet, show where these formulas are located on that sheet.

Activity 3: Areas of Right Triangles

Students who have a solid grasp of the material explore finding the areas of right triangles. Hand out triangles, *Blackline Master 14*, to each pair of students. Ask students to cut and trace Triangles A, B, C, and D onto the sq. cm grid paper on p. 74 (*Student Book*) and then to create a rectangle based on each of the triangles. Have them check their work by seeing whether the original triangle shape fits in both halves of the rectangle.

Students check their work by seeing whether the original triangle fits in both halves of the rectangle.

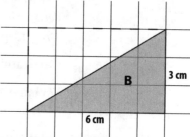

Ask:

 What is the area of each of the triangles?

Encourage students to try different methods. After everyone has determined the areas of the four triangles (A = 4.5 sq. cm, B = 9 sq. cm, C = 5 sq. cm, and D = 12.5 sq. cm), ask them to show their methods.

They might say the following:

> I counted the square centimeters in the rectangle, then divided by two.
>
> I multiplied the length of the rectangle by its width, then divided by two.
>
> I took half the area of the rectangle.
>
> *lw/2*
>
> I counted the whole square centimeters inside the triangle and then pieced together the portions.
>
> I multiplied one side of the triangle by the other, then divided by two. (If students use this method, ask which side they used. It is important that they use the sides adjacent to the right angle.)

If no one mentions finding half the area of the rectangle, ask:

 What do you see when you compare the area of the triangle with the area of the rectangle?

When you are certain that everyone sees the relationship, ask pairs to determine the areas of Triangles E and F without cutting them out or using the grid paper. This will require locating the right angle and measuring the adjacent sides with a ruler.

Have students share solutions and methods. If there is disagreement, ask students to check areas by using the grid paper (E = 7.5 sq. cm, F = 18 sq. cm).

Ask:

 On which sides is it important to focus?

Conclude that one has to be careful to use the two sides adjacent to the right angle because they are the sides of the imagined rectangle.

Ask students to relate what they did using mathematical language, for example, "half the area of the rectangle" or "length times width divided by 2." Some students might know area equals half the base times height ($A = 1/2\ bh$). Test the formulas against the examples to confirm that both procedures work.

Summary Discussion

Discuss with students what they want to remember from this lesson.

💬 **What is a quick way to figure out the area of a rectangle? A right triangle?**

💬 **What is a quick way to figure out the perimeter of a rectangle? A triangle?**

💬 **How could you handle a situation that asks for area, perimeter, or missing information about length or width if you do not recall the formula?**

💬 **What do you think is most important to remember from class today?**

Ask students to record two things they want to remember about finding missing information about rectangles in *Reflections* (*Student Book*, p. 155).

◎ Practice

Missing Measurements, p. 72
For practice finding area, perimeter, or dimensions.

More Complex Shapes, p. 77
For practice finding area and perimeter of irregular shapes.

Von's Kitchen, p. 79
For practice finding area and perimeter using two different strategies.

Areas of More Right Triangles, p. 82

⊘ Extension

Area and Perimeter Challenges, p. 81
For practice finding area and perimeter for squares.

⊞ Test Practice

Test Practice, p. 83

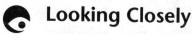

Looking Closely

Observe whether students are able to

Find missing dimensions, area, and perimeter of rectangles

What do students do once grid lines are eliminated? Students may make sketches or use division or an algebraic approach to find missing information. Note which students have efficient strategies, and call on them to explain their steps. This could help students who are struggling. A drawing with labels and possibly tick marks is the best intermediate step to using the formula with no support.

Use the formula to calculate perimeter of a rectangle without measuring four sides

Do students use the formulas for perimeter and area?

Are they able to connect their strategies for finding perimeter and area with the formulas? If the formulas are off-putting and substitution feels too foreign, write the formula with the familiar "times" sign and words (2 × length + 2 × width = Perimeter, rather than $2l + 2w = P$).

Extend what is known about calculating the area of a rectangle to calculate the area of a right triangle

Are students curious about finding the area and perimeter of other shapes? If students are confident finding the area and perimeter of rectangles, encourage them to investigate the area of a right triangle by doubling it to form a rectangle. For students who have trouble seeing this, use the square and right triangle from the shape set. Remind students of the relationship they observed when ordering shapes by area. Use a right triangle and its mirror image to demonstrate again how a triangle's area is half that of a rectangle's.

WHAT TO LOOK FOR IN *LESSON 7*	WHO STANDS OUT? (LIST STUDENTS' INITIALS)			NOTES FOR NEXT STEPS
	STRONG	ADEQUATE	NEEDS WORK	
Concept Development • Finds area of rectangle using grid paper • Finds perimeter of rectangle using grid paper • Finds area and perimeter of rectangles without grid paper • Translates statements to formulas for area and perimeter of rectangles • Finds area of a right triangle using a rectangle as a reference				
Expressive Capacity • Writes statements about area and perimeter • Generalizes from table to statements about area and perimeter of rectangles • Writes a rule that relates area of a right triangle with area of a rectangle				
Use of Tools • Draws rectangles on grid paper • Draws rectangles on blank paper, using tick marks for units				
Background Knowledge • Refers to formulas of rectangle area and perimeter • Knows area formulas for rectangles and right triangles				

Rationale

Adults often have vague or partial recollections of formulas they once heard in school. Having opportunities to visualize, represent, and explain area and perimeter and to derive the formulas themselves helps students solidify their understanding.

Math Background

In geometry there is usually a way to see how the rules or formulas connect to words and pictures. The formula is a shorthand way of describing the pattern. It is also a universal language representation for the rule. Mathematicians like to be efficient, so they use not only formulas, but also special notation.

$$A = l \times w$$
or
$$A = l(w)$$

Right triangles fit comfortably inside of rectangles. Picture a rectangle. Connect two opposite corners with a diagonal line.

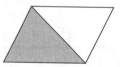

$$A = (\tfrac{1}{2}) l \times w$$

Now the rectangle is composed of two right triangles. The space inside remains unchanged, although the diagonal has split it into two equal parts. The two triangles have equal areas. So the area for one triangle is half the area of the rectangle. Hence the $A = 1/2\ l \times w$ or $A = 1/2\ b \times h$ formulas for area of a triangle.

The right triangle is a specific case, not the general case.

This lesson deals only with the specific case of the area of a right triangle because of its relationship to the rectangle. But the general formula for the area of a triangle ($A = 1/2\ bh$) is usually shown by its relationship to the area of the parallelogram.

A triangle can be seen as half a parallelogram. When a parallelogram is not rectangular (a rectangle is a specific case of a parallelogram), the area is found by multiplying one side of the shape (the base) by the height, which is not a side but the perpendicular line from one base to the other. Sometimes the height is drawn inside the figure, and other times outside.

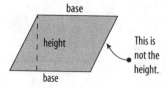

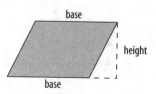

Therefore the rectangle's area can be used to show its relationship to a parallelogram's area.

The areas are equal.

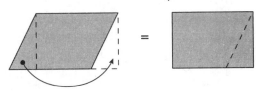

Any triangle can be shown as half that of a parallelogram with the same base and height.

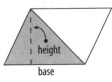

Facilitation

Students may recall the formulas for finding area and perimeter and be able to call upon their knowledge of multiplication to find them. These students will complete their work quickly and should be encouraged to try the remaining four rectangles on the chart.

Making the Lesson Easier

Replace *Activity 3* with one of the practices.

Making the Lesson Harder

Have students explore the area of triangles in general, not only right triangles. Use shapes from the Shape Set (*Blackline Masters 2* and *3*).

In multi-level classes, students who struggled with basic math concepts benefited from the approach that gradually built toward perimeter and area formulas.

During observations, I realized some students saw the numbers indicating length and width next to a rectangle as random. After a lot of work on grid paper, Mina and Jan began to see those numbers as a shortcut to drawing rows and columns of squares. The numbers became meaningful. I saw Jan begin to use numbers in her own sketches to figure out her answer.

Martha Merson, Observer
Project Place, Boston, MA

Students seemed to be a little frustrated to have learned the grid-paper method of area and perimeter and then to have to change everything they had learned to complete the process. "Why are we doing this without grid paper?" was one comment I heard. One student even had some grid paper in her bag that she tried to use. After a bit, the students caught on and realized they had a more organized method for computing these problems. "Why didn't you just teach us this in the first place?" two students asked. I explained to them that if I had given them formulas to start with, they wouldn't understand what area and perimeter really were; they would just know another math formula. "So there is a reason you are making us do all of this work then," one student stated.

Mindy Harrison
Rock Valley College Adult Education Center, Rockford, IL

Conversion Experiences

> *What would you measure in inches? In feet? In yards?*

Synopsis

This is the first of two lessons in which students use Standard English units—inches, feet, and yards— and become familiar with converting them. In *Lesson 9*, students also work with square inches, square feet, and square yards.

1. Students name items they would measure in inches, feet, or yards.

2. The whole group defines "converting," lists occasions that might necessitate conversion, and completes a quick assessment of unit equivalents units.

3. Small groups measure the dimensions and perimeters of three rectangles in either inches, feet, or yards.

4. Groups post perimeter measurements and debate whether all measurements (reported in various units) are equivalent.

5. The class discusses the accuracy of the measurements and articulates steps or rules for converting between units.

Objectives

· Use Standard English linear units to measure perimeters
· Verify that different units of measure can be equivalent
· Convert between units, choosing the correct operation

Materials/Prep

· Markers
· Masking tape
· Measuring tapes, marked in inches
· Rulers, marked in inches
· Yardsticks

Prepare a transparency or enlarged version of the table from *It's All in How You Measure*, p. 86. Use masking tape to make three rectangles with the following dimensions on the floor or walls. Label them Rectangles 1, 2, and 3, respectively, but do not indicate the measurements:

- Rectangle 1   18" by 3'
- Rectangle 2   3' by 6'
- Rectangle 3   6' by 9'

Photocopy and cut up cards for *Unit Conversion Quick Assessment, Blackline Master 15*. You will need two per student, one at the beginning of class and one again at the end.

Prepare chalkboard or newsprint as follows:

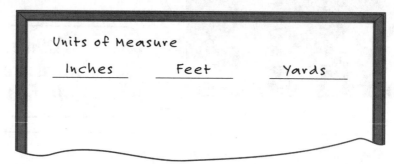

Opening Discussion

The warm-up questions and activities below are designed to accomplish the following:

- Tap into students' background knowledge
- Check for individuals' sense of linear units
- Define and set up the motivation for unit conversions

Refer to the chart you prepared and say:

We will make a list of things we would measure in feet, inches, or yards. Name anything you bought recently that came in feet, inches, or yards.

List the items. If few students volunteer, present a few items, such as a roll of tape or rope, and ask about each:

What unit(s) would you use to measure this?

Ask the class why the unit chosen is appropriate to measure the item listed. Distinguish between square units and linear units.

When you state your height, how do you say it? Why would you never give your height in yards?

Have you ever gone to get your hair cut and asked the hairstylist to take off an inch? Why not tell the person cutting your hair to trim off 1/12 of a foot?

Ask students to show their ideas for an inch, a foot, and a yard. Everyone can find and record a body part that is approximately equivalent to these lengths (finger joint for an inch, forearm or person's foot for a foot, or the length from the nose to the finger tip with the arm outstretched for a yard). Have students check their body parts with a ruler or yardstick.

Whose finger joint is exactly an inch?

Whose foot is exactly a foot?

Whose nose to finger tip measurement is exactly a yard?

Tell the class that sometimes you are given a measurement in one unit when you want it in another. For instance, you may want to buy something (draw on student examples from the list), and you know the amount of material you need in yards, but the store clerk asks how many feet you need. Someone has to convert the measurement.

What does it mean to "convert" the measurement?

Listen to one or two explanations, or offer your own if no one volunteers.

Take a quick assessment of student knowledge about converting Standard English linear units by distributing one of the cards from *Unit Conversion Quick Assessment* to each student. Ask the following questions in order, and collect or have students post their answers after each question:

How many inches are in a foot?

How many feet are in a yard?

How many inches are in a yard?

Glance over the responses. If there is general disagreement, you may wish to take the time to explore equivalent units (see *Lesson Commentary*, p. 96). Otherwise, group the responses and report to the class that most people seem to know the answers. Write the equivalencies on the board so that all students have the correct information:

- 12 inches = one foot
- 3 feet = one yard
- 36 inches = one yard

Reinforce this information by asking volunteers to show the equivalents on a yardstick, tape measure, and ruler.

Point out the possible ways to write abbreviations for the different units, for example, in., ", ft., ', and yd.

Activity: It's All in How You Measure

Divide the class into three groups. Assign each group its own unit of measure: Group A, inches; Group B, feet; and Group C, yards. Large classes might have two groups for each unit of measure.

Read the directions for *It's All in How You Measure* p. 86. Each group will find the dimensions and perimeter of the three taped rectangles in the unit they were assigned. Let groups choose their tools from yardsticks, 12-inch rulers, and tape measures (Problems 1 and 2).

Before groups begin to measure, ask:

 Which group do you think will have the largest numbers? Which group do you think will have the smallest numbers?

Discuss the reasoning for predictions.

Heads Up!

Remind students not to include the tape itself when they measure the rectangle; the tape merely outlines the rectangle they are measuring.

Post the enlarged copy of the chart: "It's All in How You Measure," p. 86. As students calculate the rectangles' perimeters, they fill in the group chart and their own charts.

Heads Up!

Do not correct groups' work on perimeter measurements yet. The discussion will be livelier if students talk about inconsistencies.

When the chart is complete, assign Problems 2–6.

 With your group, review the data in the chart. Your job is to verify whether all the perimeters listed for each shape are equal. Be prepared to show how you know. You cannot re-measure any of the rectangles, but you can refer to any of the measuring tools as you work.

If groups finish early, assign Problems 7 and 8.

Summary Discussion

After all groups have completed Problems 1–6, pull the class together to review their work. Ask the same questions for each rectangle:

 Does everyone agree that the perimeter measures for Rectangle 1 are correct? What makes you think so? (or) **What makes you disagree?**

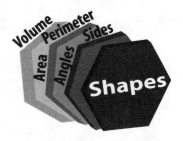

Encourage students to use tools and demonstrations to support their findings.

Ask the same questions about Rectangles 2 and 3.

To double-check the class's understanding, write the width of Rectangle 3 (72″) on the chalkboard. Ask students about their methods, turning attention to the operation used. Write down students' answers.

How would you convert this measurement to feet?

How would you convert this measurement to yards?

Then write the length in yards for Rectangle 3 (3 yd.). Ask:

How would you convert this measurement to inches?

How would you convert this measurement to feet?

Again, focus on the steps. Write down the rule in students' words.

Push for a generalization about which operation (division) lends itself to moving from smaller units to larger ones and which works best for converting larger units to smaller ones (multiplication).

If there is time, check on the processes students used to reach solutions for Problem 8, (*Student Book*, p. 88).

Distribute new copies of the strip from *Unit Conversion: Quick Assessment*, *Blackline Master 17*, for another quick assessment.

Practice

Home Measurements, p. 89
For practice measuring objects around the house.

Units of Measure, p. 89
For practice relating linear units to body parts or objects familiar to students.

Keeping Units Straight, p.89
For practice converting between units.

Extension

Conversion Match, p. 90

The Foreman's Problem, p. 92
For conversion and perimeter work.

Test Practice

Test Practice, p. 94

Looking Closely

Observe whether students are able to

Use Standard English linear units to measure perimeters

What strategies do students use to find perimeter in inches, feet, or yards? If necessary, refer students to their work from previous lessons to find the steps they have used in the past or a formula.

Are students comfortable using a ruler, tape measure, or yardstick? To what tools do they gravitate? Some students will benefit from practice with measuring. If they are struggling, suggest a tool that will facilitate their work. Make sure students locate zero on their measuring tools and start their measurements there or compensate accordingly. Help students find zero on the different tools and align the tools with the items they are measuring. Make sure students are rounding to the nearest inch. Point out the number and the long, thick line designating inches on the tools they are using.

Verify that different units of measure can be equivalent

Do students grasp that, although the numbers for different units of measurement are not alike, the measurements are equal? Have students who are struggling with converting feet into yards or inches, for instance, measure one side in all three units. Ask them if the size of the rectangle has changed. Point out that if a person's height were recorded first in feet and inches and then just in inches, the height would not change, although the numbers would look different.

Convert between units, choosing the correct operation

Do students freeze up when they encounter a measurement, such as 40 or 400 inches, which they need to convert to another unit? Emphasize grouping or bundling. For example, ask students how many inches are in a foot. Then ask them whether they can make groups of 12, count up by 12, or estimate how many groups of 12 would be in 40 or 400.

Ask students how they could solve the problem using a calculator. They could try different operations and check their results. How do they interpret the remainder? 40 inches = 3.4 ft. or 1.11111... yd. or 3.33333... ft. How does that compare with 3′4″? Why doesn't the calculator screen read 3.4?

WHAT TO LOOK FOR IN *LESSON 8*	WHO STANDS OUT? (LIST STUDENTS' INITIALS)			NOTES FOR NEXT STEPS
	STRONG	ADEQUATE	NEEDS WORK	
Concept Development • Measures accurately • Finds perimeters using linear units • Compares measurements in inches with measurements in feet • Compares measurements in feet with measurements in yards • Converts between units				
Expressive Capacity • Distinguishes between units				
Use of Tools • Uses rulers, yardsticks, and tape measures to measure to the nearest whole inch • Illustrates relationship between measurements using tools • Uses the calculator to convert between units				
Background Knowledge • Knows numerical equivalents • Knows benchmarks for each measurement unit				

Rationale

Conversion of units is central to understanding measurement. Familiarity with all units enables students not only to choose the best unit for the situation but also to simplify comparisons or problems by establishing consistent units.

Math Background

Some say that numbers were first used to count, then to measure. Body parts were used to measure lengths. English Standard units derived from these early, approximate measures. An inch was about the width of a man's thumb, though in the 14th century, King Edward II of England declared it equaled three grains of barley laid end to end. The length of a man's foot was about 12 inches. King Henry I of England decreed in the 12th century that the yard would be the measurement from the tip of *his* nose to the end of *his* thumb when his arm was stretched out.

Converting units of measure is a proportional exercise, although it is not treated formally so here. It is key to understanding unit equivalents.

Facilitation

Provide the history of the English Standard units (above), and encourage students to see how closely their personal body measurements match the king's guidelines: thumb width, foot length, and distance from nose tip to thumb end on an outstretched arm.

Making the Lesson Easier

If students struggle with the idea of conversion, talk through examples using coin exchanges, for example, 10 pennies in a dime, 5 nickels in a quarter. Practice converting with physical objects. Distribute tape measures, rulers, and yardsticks. Ask students to explore how many of each measuring tool fit into the others, report their findings, and establish the equivalents.

Call out conversion requests: "Three feet equals how many yards? Two feet equals how many inches? Forty-eight inches equals how many feet?"

Accept alternatives to multiplication when changing feet to inches—for example, repeated addition, or using mental math strategies of 10's and 1's (12 + 12 + 12 is the same as 10 + 10 + 10 + 2 + 2 + 2). Allow the use of the calculator to verify addition.

Making the Lesson Harder

Have all groups use a tape measure. If the tape measure is marked only in inches, this forces the "feet" and "yard" groups to convert immediately.

For *Activity 1*, create rectangles with messier measurements, such as a 48″ by 42″ rectangle or a one-meter square.

Move to the *Extension* problems after the *Opening Discussion*.

Predicting the unit size after conversion was a puzzle that motivated the activity.

Given the measuring tools, everyone drew an inch. Immediately we had to discuss where to place the tool. My measuring tapes are bound by a metal piece that obscures zero and the first half inch. One ruler started at zero; another had a margin of space and then had a line marking zero.

We also drew a line for a foot, by going diagonally the length of an 8.5″ x 11″ piece of paper. One student thought a foot would be equal to two of her feet in length. I handed her the 12-inch ruler and told her to check it out. The students all found a body-part approximation for a foot and wrote it down, as well as the number of inches in a foot.

Whose group would have the biggest numbers? Only Alicia, a student who has her share of struggles, said that the "yard" group would have a smaller number. The others were against her, and so later it was great to see she was right. It would prove a memorable moment because in future classes everyone remembered, and I could not trick them again.

Students made the measuring task harder for themselves in their choice of tools. The group doing yards had a 60-inch measuring tape. They had to do some additional math to figure out what the lengths were. The floor in the room is covered by 12″ square tiles, but no group noticed or used this as an aid.

When I wondered aloud whether all the measurements for Rectangle 1 would be the same, students contradicted me. They assumed the numbers would not be equivalent. Then I had to clarify what I meant. They were correct; the numbers would not be the same. A rectangle's perimeter won't measure five yards and also five inches, but the amounts [for the two different measurements] would be equal. Once we had that clarified, they still believed the amounts would be different. After they checked the math, they finally began to accept the idea of equivalent amounts and agreed that with their own heights, the numbers for inches or for feet and inches should be equivalent.

Martha Merson
Guest Teacher, X-Cel Education, Dorchester, MA

9

Squarely in English

> *How is this sold: by the square inch, square foot, or square yard?*

Synopsis

In this lesson, students continue using the Standard English system of inches, feet, and yards to measure area in square units.

1. In groups, students construct square inches, square feet, or square yards.

2. Students gain experience with converting between square units.

3. Students use square units to measure the area of different objects.

4. The whole class discusses what has been learned and how they might apply it.

Objectives

- Construct and describe standard square units of measure: inches, feet, and yards
- Convert among square inches, square feet, and square yards
- Connect area with square unit measures

Materials/Prep

- Calculators
- Extra square units, especially square inches and square feet (bought or homemade tiles, for instance)
- Materials to cut up, e.g., construction paper, manila folders, or paper bags
- Measuring tools, e.g., protractors, rulers, yard sticks, and tape measures in centimeters and inches
- Scissors

Post a few advertisements around the room. See samples in *Blackline Master 16*, and supplement with local ones.

Opening Discussion

Review the linear units of measurement the class has used thus far. Students can demonstrate with hands or rulers.

Show me one inch.

Show me one foot.

Show me half a foot.

Show me six inches.

Tell me something you would measure in feet.

Call attention to the ads around the room, and tell students:

Pick one that is hard for you to understand or to visualize. By the end of class today you should be able to picture, draw, or explain it to others.

Give an overview of the lesson by saying:

You are about to become an expert in a unit of measurement—either the square yard, the square foot, or the square inch.

Activity: Squarely in English

Divide students into pairs or small groups. Assign each group a square unit to investigate. Every group needs measuring tools and materials to cut up. Groups can consult each other, especially when figuring out conversions.

Heads Up!

Each group will have to create squares. To do so, they will need to construct 90° angles. Students may use protractors or trace the corner of a book.

Group 1

- Construct at least 12 square inches.
- Figure out how many square inches are in a square foot.
- Measure the area of one object in square inches.
- Sketch the results to share with the group.
- Recommend a way to remember the size of an inch and a square inch.

Group 2: Construct at least 10 square feet.

- Calculate how many square feet are in a square yard.
- Measure the area of one object in square feet.
- Sketch the results to share with the group.
- Recommend a way to remember the size of a foot and a square foot.

Group 3: Construct at least three square yards.

- Figure out how many square inches fit into a square yard.
- Measure the area of one object in square yards.
- Sketch the results to share with the group.
- Recommend a way to remember the size of a yard and of a square yard.

Group 4: If there are enough people, ask one group to construct square centimeters as a way to contrast the size of square centimeters and square inches.

Heads Up!

Have students check with you before they cut their square units. Make sure the angles are right angles and the edges are equal in length.

Offer extra square inches to groups; no one should have to make 144 square inches. As students work, pose questions that ask for predictions. For example, once they have covered a complete square foot with square inches, can they estimate how many square inches are in a square yard? How would they calculate the amount?

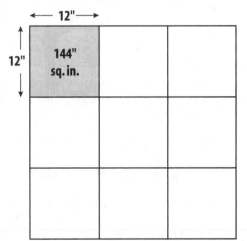

As the groups finish, ask them to choose something in the class to measure with their square units. For example, have students find the area of the chalkboard, the area of a window, or the area of a piece of paper. Students record the measurements and then as a group convert them to the other units. They can work out the math or use calculators. Alternatively, ask students to try mental math (breaking down numbers into 10's and 1's) and to check their work with another method. Ask:

 How do I know whether to divide or multiply when converting?

Summary Discussion

Each group presents its work. Make sure students explain

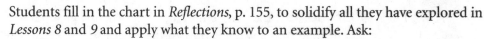

- How they figured out the number of one unit there was in another;

- What other ways they could have used to figure this out.

Students fill in the chart in *Reflections*, p. 155, to solidify all they have explored in *Lessons 8* and *9* and apply what they know to an example. Ask:

 How would we find the number of square inches in four square feet or the number of square feet in three square yards?

Write the steps in words, and make sure students know how to convert from one unit to another with a calculator. If there is any hesitation, return to the concrete square units students made. After students fill in the chart on the *Reflections* page, ask:

 What do square inches, feet, and yards measure—area or perimeter?

 What shape is everyone's final product? Why? (Reinforce the squareness of square units.)

If no one mentions it, state that square units are the standard unit for measuring area regardless of the shape.

Direct attention to the ads around the room, each showing a number or a measurement. Ask students to convey the size of the measurement. They can explain, draw, or act out the measurement (with or without their tools and square units). Keep the focus on the math in the phrase and the space being described by asking:

 How many square units are there?

 What could the length and width measures be for a space that size?

Practice

Choose a Unit, p. 97

Roll Out the Carpet, p. 98
For practice converting with cost comparison.

The Better Deal, p. 99
For practice converting with cost comparison.

San Diego Construction Company, p. 100

Area Measurements, p. 101
For practice finding dimensions and area.

 ## Extension

Checkerboard Paint Job, p. 102

 ## Test Practice

Test Practice, p. 103

 ## Looking Closely

Observe whether students are able to

Construct and describe standard square units of measure: inches, feet, and yards

If students are not using a ruler accurately, suggest they practice taking more measurements. If students are not making right angles accurately, remind them lines should be perpendicular. They could trace right angles with the angle demonstrator or use corners of paper or cardboard.

If the group constructing the square yard can go to a larger space or outdoors, they will have more space to move their square yard around and can measure larger areas.

Convert among square inches, square feet, and square yards

Do students see that the number of square inches in a square foot, for example, is 144? Guesses are likely to be 12, 48, or perhaps 96. As students lay out the one-inch square tiles, they should begin to see that their area formula (12 x 12) will yield the answer. Whenever the conversation begins to get abstract, refer back to the manipulatives students constructed, and revisit the formulas for nine square feet in a square yard and 144 square inches in a square foot.

Connect area with square unit measures

Does students' language reflect their awareness of linear units vs. square units? Continue to ask, "How many of *what*?" if you hear answers given with numbers and no units. Give similar feedback if incorrect units or no units are given on practice sheets.

WHAT TO LOOK FOR IN *LESSON 9*	WHO STANDS OUT? (LIST STUDENTS' INITIALS)			NOTES FOR NEXT STEPS
	STRONG	ADEQUATE	NEEDS WORK	
Concept Development • Distinguishes among square units: square inches, square feet, and square yards • Expands idea of conversions to include linear and square units • Chooses the correct operation to perform conversions among units • Uses appropriate strategy to convert among units				
Expressive Capacity • Uses unit labels appropriately to describe amounts • Describes differences between linear units and square units				
Use of Tools • Uses rulers to measure inches, feet, and yards • Uses calculator to check or calculate conversions				
Background Knowledge • Has experience purchasing items in square units				

Rationale

Students often have difficulty converting among units. Their operation sense is shaky because their ability to visualize units and the relationships among them is not well developed. This lesson directs students to look closely at the relationships among square inches, square feet, and square yards; only then are the operations to convert among units introduced.

Math Background

Linear units are used to measure distances, dimensions, and perimeters, all one-dimensional. Square units are used for area, which is two-dimensional. The definitions for and steps to find area and perimeter were developed in previous lessons, so the concepts are not new. Conversion among Standard English units, however, is a multi-step process that involves first recalling the unit equivalencies, then multiplying or dividing. Realizing that 1 square foot is *not* 12 square inches is difficult for some students because the "1 foot = 12 inches" equivalence is so engrained. Visual representations of rectangles or squares are helpful in understanding conversion. By not only seeing area compared with perimeter but also having a tactile experience of area using manipulatives, students are reminded that a square foot, for example, is really a 12-inch by 12-inch object.

Knowing the equivalencies, the next decision students must make is which operation to use. Situations calling for conversion are of two types: converting to a larger unit from a smaller one (e.g., sq. ft. into sq. yd.) or to a smaller unit from a larger one (e.g., sq. ft. into sq. in.). For many, the idea of going from a smaller unit to a larger unit using division is counterintuitive, as is using multiplication to go from a larger unit to a smaller unit. Keeping track of conversions by using a table will help students keep the relationships among units clear. The idea of multiplying or dividing can emerge as a shortcut to setting up a table and working incrementally.

Facilitation

The easiest group task is the first; the hardest is the third. Either group students who are struggling with strong partners, or assign them the easiest task.

Making the Lesson Easier

If you are running out of time, students can pick something to measure and make an estimate but not actually measure during this session. Keep the focus on the relative size of the units. Once the class has agreed on conversions among square inches, square feet, and square yards, students create a poster with examples of the square units and notes about making conversions. Post it in the classroom for students to use as a reference.

Making the Lesson Harder

Refer to the exponent used to denote square units. Point out the relationship between square units and squared numbers. When asking students how to find the number of square inches in a square yard, for example, write $12^2 \times 3^2$ along with 144×9.

Making sense of unit conversion in one classroom.

I asked one group to measure the classroom floor in square feet and the other group to measure the mirror on one wall in square yards. The floor group got a big hint when I suggested they check the size of the floor tiles. One student correctly guessed they were each one square foot. Another did not believe her until he personally checked by placing the square foot made during class against one of the floor tiles.

Once students had posted their measurements, I asked them to convert each measurement so we would have the figures in square inches, feet, and yards. "Will the number of square yards or square feet be bigger?" I asked. Some students remembered from a previous class that the number of yards is smaller than the number of feet.

Once students knew the square yards and the square feet, I realized they could find the square inches in two different ways. One group found out the chalkboard was 6 sq. yd., or 54 sq. ft. To find the inches, they could have multiplied the square yards (6) by 1,296. They chose instead to multiply the square feet (54) by 144.

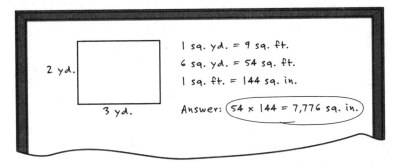

1 sq. yd. = 9 sq. ft.
6 sq. yd. = 54 sq. ft.
1 sq. ft. = 144 sq. in.

Answer: (54 × 144 = 7,776 sq. in.)

Martha Merson
Guest Teacher at X-Cel Education, Boston, MA

The teacher confronts students' confusion over the operation to use when converting among units.

I started the class with a review of what we did last week. I asked the class to outline in the air an inch, a foot, and a yard. When I asked them to show a square inch, I held up a square-inch tile I had on hand. I also had on hand a linoleum square-foot tile and a square yard of fabric. I held up the appropriate tile as they outlined the unit.

To review the conversions, I asked: "How many square inches in a square foot; how many square feet in a square yard; and how many square inches in a square yard?" The students answered these questions easily; but then I asked, "If I wanted to change square feet to square inches, what would I do?" They all knew the answer was 144 but could not decide whether they should multiply or divide.

I help up a square-foot tile and a square-inch tile. Once they saw the size of the tiles again, they knew there would be more square inches than square feet, so they realized they had to multiply. We worked through a few more questions like that. Each time I held up the squares in question.

Marilyn Moses
Brockton Adult Learning Center, Brockton, MA

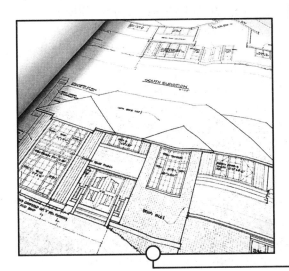

10

Scale Down

> *What's the scale?*

Synopsis

In this lesson, students will use different methods to make scale drawings. In *Lesson 4*, students explored features of similar shapes, an important aspect of scale. The result of making a scale drawing is a similar shape. Here the emphasis is on changing the measurement unit to produce a scale drawing.

1. The whole class makes a sketch of a door.

2. Groups use grid paper of different sizes to make a scale drawing of the door.

3. Students look at how similarity, proportion, and practicality all play a role in drawing to scale and compare drawings to see which appear to scale.

4. Students list steps for completing a scale drawing.

Objectives

- Make a scale drawing of an object
- Outline steps for drawing to scale

Materials/Prep

- Grid paper of different sizes: inch, 3/4-inch, 1/2-inch, 1/4-inch, and cm (*Blackline Masters 25–29*).

- Maps, both drawn to scale and not drawn to scale

- Measuring tools

- Paper of different dimensions: 3″ x 5″ cards or Post-it Notes™; 8 ½″ x 11″ or larger sheets of paper (but not as large as the door)

Write questions on newsprint, and post for students to refer to during the activity.

- What did you do to get started? What did you have to consider?
- How did you decide on the scale?
- How certain do you feel about the accuracy of your drawings? How could you check to see whether you are right?

Opening Discussion

Begin by asking students:

💬 **Have you ever used a map, a theater seating chart, or a furniture plan for a room? They are all examples of ways something large can be shown with a smaller scaled representation.**

💬 **Does anyone know the definition of "scale drawing"?**

Introduce **scale** with this explanation: *All the distances or measurements in a scale drawing are in the same proportion to one another as in real life.* Emphasize the idea of reducing something large to a size where it can be represented on a piece of paper or a table. Explain that architects make models with all the measurements scaled down so that the relationships among width, length, depth, and height are all the same as they will be for the actual building.

✺ Activity 1: Sketch the Door

In the second activity, students will do a careful drawing to scale, but in this first activity, ask students simply to sketch the door.

💬 **Look closely at the doorway. Think about the shape. Draw a sketch of the door on your paper. Make your sketch as close to the actual shape as you can.**

Ask students to compare drawings with a partner What is the same? What is different? Whose drawing appears more accurate? Why? Before moving on, summarize: Scale keeps relationships in balance.

✺ Activity 2: A Mathematician Uses Scale

Together or in groups

- Read about the mathematician's approach to a task that calls for drawing to scale, p. 102;
- Figure out and list the steps outlined.

Distribute various size grid paper. Point out which door students will draw to scale. Each group will

- Follow the steps to make at least two scale drawings for the door you designated;
- Prepare to explain their steps to the whole class.

Heads Up!

If the door's dimensions result in fractional units, suggest students round to whole numbers or use smaller units of measurement.

Review directions in *Student Book,* p. 107. Have measuring tools available. As students work, ask them to check whether the shapes they have drawn to scale are similar to the door. In addition, check whether the scales they have chosen maximize the space on the page.

Before groups finish, ask students to write the scale they used on their drawings, for example, 1 inch = 1 foot. Students can exchange drawings and check each other's work.

When groups report back, ask students to explain their steps. List steps that students took to solve the problem.

💬 **What did you do to get started? What did you have to consider?**

💬 **How did you decide on the scale?**

Follow up with questions such as the following:

💬 **Did you count the number of squares? What are the number of squares for the length and width of your grid paper?**

💬 **How certain do you feel about your drawings? How could you check to see whether you are right?**

Drawing to scale is an open-ended activity with more than one right answer. Students compare the drawings done with different scales and also compare their sketches with the scale drawings. How closely do they match? Ask:

💬 **How can these drawings be accurate but look different?**

💬 **What is the same? What is different about them?**

Test students' understanding by asking:

💬 **What happens if you choose one scale for the width and a different scale for the length?** (The shape will not be similar to the original.)

Summary Discussion

 If I gave you something large to scale down, how would you do it?

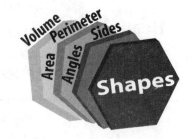

With the students, formulate a checklist similar to the one below that they can consult when they draw to scale.

- Measure the object to find the size and the relation of its dimensions.
- Think about the size of your paper or the size that you want the scaled version to be.
- Look at the longest dimension. Will it fit on your paper if you change units?
- Try different numbers. Is there a number by which you can shrink both the length and width that is easy (for example, divide by 2, 5, or 10)?
- Check to make sure the scaled version will fit on the paper and that your new drawing has the same shape as the original.

Students record the steps and their thoughts in *Reflections* (*Student Book*, p. 157).

- Display or distribute maps. Ask:

 What did the mapmakers have to think about? Why does a map give us a sense of where places are in relationship to one another?

Ask students to prepare for an assessment (*Interim Assessment 2: A Fresh Look*). Brainstorm a list of the concepts covered in the lessons so far. Advise students to review their practice sheets and vocabulary. This assessment focuses on the perimeter and area and consists of two activities: (1) done in groups and (2) done individually.

Practice

Scale Drawings, p. 108

Shrinking Doors, p. 109
For practice deciding scale.

All About Shapes, p. 111

Extension

Enlarge It!, p. 113

Test Practice

Test Practice, p. 114

Looking Closely

Observe whether students are able to

Make a scale drawing of an object

Do students pick a factor for scaling that works with the size of their grid paper? Students are likely to become frustrated if they choose a scale that exceeds the size of their paper. For example, if the door is 86 inches in height, a scale of 1 inch = 1 cm will not fit on a piece of 19 x 30 cm grid paper. In this case, ask: "Is there something else each square could represent? What if you try having one centimeter equal three inches?" Encourage students to experiment, choosing the largest dimension and keeping track of what scales they have tried. Practicing a few times will help them internalize the process, and it will become increasingly easy for them to imagine what scale to use before putting pencil to paper.

Outline steps for drawing to scale

Are students able to read a description and distill a set of steps? Can they reconstruct their processes to list the steps? Ask students to relate their actions to the mathematician's description in *Activity 2.*

For some students, scale may trigger recollection of work with proportion. These students may want to use equivalent fractions and should use them as a system for checking their work. You could express the relationships in natural language (one centimeter for every foot, for instance), whether students choose to use proportion or not.

WHAT TO LOOK FOR IN *LESSON 10*	WHO STANDS OUT? (LIST STUDENTS' INITIALS)			NOTES FOR NEXT STEPS
	STRONG	ADEQUATE	NEEDS WORK	
Concept Development • Makes a drawing of an object to scale • Makes a drawing of an object using a different scale • Recognizes when a drawing is and is not to scale • Knows the steps to take to make a drawing to scale				
Expressive Capacity • Explains the scale used for drawing an object • Articulates how an object looks when it is to scale as compared to when it is *not* to scale • Explains the steps for drawing an object to scale				
Use of Tools • Uses grid to draw objects to scale				
Background Knowledge • Knows about scale from reading maps, looking at floor plans, etc.				

Rationale

In general, sketching is a helpful problem-solving tool. When the problem involves something too large or cumbersome for a person to physically handle, drawing to scale can help make sense of the problem and lead to a solution. Interpreting scale drawings is useful for reading maps and instruction manuals and solving real-life problems in construction, as well as for solving GED test problems.

Math Background

Drawing to scale does not require a lot of number operations, but it does require a sense of proportion.

Many people make seemingly arbitrary decisions about scale—for example, assigning one square of a grid to equal one foot. As long as the change in units is kept constant, the result will be to scale. If length is scaled to inches, the width should also be scaled to inches. If one dimension is scaled to a different unit than another, a distorted picture will result.

Facilitation

Making the Lesson Easier

Use one size of grid paper in *Activity 2*. Model the activity. Then assign pairs or groups to work on a second scale drawing on a different size grid paper.

Making the Lesson Harder

Ask each group to draw the same thing to scale on grid paper of different sizes (e.g., 1/4-inch, 1/2-inch, 1 inch, 1 cm). Ask students to comment on which size made the task easiest and to speculate why. Have students draw to scale a door that has a length or width in mixed units or fractional measurements.

Use fractional notation to record how the original and the scale drawing relate. Keep the natural language and notation closely linked. For example:

- Door length in life is 7 ft.; door length on paper is 7 in.
- Door width in life is 3 ft.; door width on paper is 3 in.

The students outline their steps, highlighting the experiments they tried in order to find a reasonable scale.

Indira reports for her group:

"Our steps:

    1. Get grid paper.

    2. Count how many squares down, how many across.

    3. Measure the door by feet: $w = 3'$, $l = 7'$

Each block = 1/2 foot, so the width is 6 blocks.

Length is 14 squares down.

Therefore: 3 feet = 36"; 7 feet = 84"."

Student: "How did you choose one block for a half-foot?"

Teacher: "Why didn't you make each block equal one foot or one block equal eight inches?"

Javier: "Our group measured the door in inches: 36" x 84". We counted all the squares on the grid paper. One square for one inch is no good. We counted, but the door wouldn't fit. Then we tried one block for two inches."

Teacher: "How many squares do they need?"

Student: "Forty-two inches."

Javier: "Still no good. What about one block for three inches? We know we had enough space for 30 inches. Eighty-four divided by 3 equals 28 squares. Then divide the width by 3 and get 12 squares."

Teacher: "Can anyone comment on the drawing?"

Student: "It's a similar shape."

Observer: "You did one square equals three inches for the length. That is good because it fits, but on the top you have more room. How about one block equals two inches for the width?"

Student: "That won't work."

Teacher: "Manuel, your group tried something like that. What happened?"

Manuel: "The shape comes out like a square not a rectangle."

Teacher (summarizing): "What does it mean to shrink something?"

Student: "Make it smaller and still get the shape."

Teacher: "Remember: What happens to one side, happens to the other side."

Marilyn Moses
Brockton Adut Learning Center, Brockton, MA

Facilitating Interim Assessment 2: A Fresh Look

> *How much material do we need?*

Synopsis

A Fresh Look is a two-part performance assessment that asks students to synthesize and apply the concepts covered thus far in the unit. The activities and review can easily take two sessions.

1. The whole class shares past experiences with home-improvement projects.

2. Students work collaboratively in groups. They measure to determine how much paint, tile, or molding they would need to buy and the costs they would incur to give the classroom a fresh look. Groups prepare their reports and scale drawings.

3. The whole class listens to the reports.

4. Students work on individualized pencil-and-paper problems in *Activity 2*.

Objectives

- Take measurements of a large space
- Convert measurements into units that allow for reasonable calculations of cost
- Present findings including a drawing to scale
- Solve perimeter, area, and measurement problems

Materials/Prep

- Calculators
- Chart paper
- Colored markers

- Measuring tapes
- Rulers
- Square-foot tile
- Yardsticks

Make copies of the *Interim Assessment 2: A Fresh Look* (*Student Book*, p. 117; *Teacher Book, Appendices*, p. 173), one copy for each student.

Opening Discussion

Give an overview of the two activities in this *Interim Assessment*. Students will use their knowledge of geometry and measurement to work on plans to freshen up the classroom and to solve problems. They will find area and perimeter in centimeters, inches, feet, and yards.

Begin by asking:

💬 **Have you ever had to paint a room? Or tile a floor? Or put molding up around a room?**

💬 **How did you decide how much material to buy?**

Allow some sharing of experiences and then say:

💬 **Instead of a home improvement project, we have a classroom improvement project. Your job is to figure out how much paint, how many tiles, or how much molding to buy to give this room a fresh look.**

💬 **Which do you think will be the most expensive job? Why?**

Listen as students make predictions. Summarize and record what they think is going to be the most expensive job.

 ## Assessment Activity 1: Fixing Up the Classroom

Heads Up!

The numbers are bigger than usual. Allow time for measuring and checking. Measure the room and complete the tasks yourself ahead of time so you have a sense of reasonable answers.

Form groups and assign one task per group (Task 1, 2, or 3). Students preview their tasks. Go over key parts of the directions, and highlight the three parts to this task:

- Plan: Fill out *Fixing Up the Classroom*.
- Measure: Take measurements, record them, sketch scale drawings, and calculate needed information.
- Report: Write and present your report.

If you intend to score the groups' work, share your guidelines ahead of time. Solicit students' input for the assessment guidelines by asking:

💬 **What would you look for in a complete report?**

As students work on the activity, issues may arise. Let students discuss and resolve issues such as

- What space is included? Students may wonder whether to include a door or closet when estimating amounts of materials.
- How exact should the measurements be? People usually round up a bit when deciding the amount of material they need to buy.

A few minutes before the end of the first session, bring the class together and ask a representative from each group to report. Ask:

💬 **What have you learned or accomplished so far?**

💬 **What did you struggle with?**

💬 **What will you do next?**

Pose the following problems, and brainstorm solutions:

- How can a drawing of the room fit on a page? One centimeter on the page cannot equal one centimeter in the room. What could one centimeter stand for?
- What should you do about unwieldy numbers or fractions? What would you do in real life? (Usually people agree they round up to a more friendly number.)
- How do you check unit conversions for accuracy?
- How do you handle remainders and decimal points that are the result of converting among units?

Remind students about their punch-lists:

- Did you include scale drawings?
- How much material will you need?
- How much will it cost?
- How did you arrive at those conclusions?
- How did you confirm your answers?

After each group presents its report to the class, ask:

💬 **What makes this estimate sound too high, too low, or about right?**

Students may bring up the need to consider waste, to calculate sales tax, or to figure in labor costs, and may offer other ideas from their experiences. All of this will enrich the discussion.

Assessment Activity 2: Home, Sweet Home

Give an overview of the focus of each task:

Task 1: Measurement

Task 2: Comparison of rectangular shapes

Task 3: Application of what you know about area and perimeter of rectangles

Ask students to complete the problems. If students have never looked at a floor plan, you may want to preview it with them. Remind students to solve the problems they can do easily and return to the more difficult ones later.

Summary Discussion

Ask students to discuss the two activities and focus on their reactions.

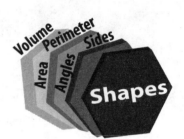

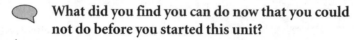 **What did you find you can do now that you could not do before you started this unit?**

 **What was hard? What was easy?**

If students thought the assessment was difficult or if they felt unprepared, ask:

How might you have prepared differently?

It is often helpful to ask if students felt they knew material that was not addressed by the assessment. Ask:

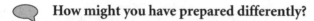 **Was there anything else you wish I had asked?**

This helps you determine what students thought the important concepts were and provides you with information for the next time you teach this unit.

👁 Looking Closely

Observe whether students are able to

Take measurements of a large space

How do students resolve questions that arise when they deal with mixed units of measurement? Number work has been kept purposely simple throughout the unit so that the focus would be on the development of geometric ideas. In this lesson, the situation is different. Students will have to make decisions about what to do, for example, when the floor of the room measures 12 feet and 2 inches by 17 feet and 3 inches. They could estimate the area as about 12 feet by 17 feet (204 sq. ft.), but they have to decide whether to round up to 210 or 215 square feet to accommodate the extra inches. Or if a window measures 30 inches by four feet, they have to choose which unit to use and how to convert.

Convert measurements into a unit that allows for reasonable calculations of cost

How do students handle unwieldy numbers? Look for student strategies including rounding, reasonable estimates, revising initial calculations, double-checking with a calculator, and keeping the figures and information organized.

Present findings including a scale drawing

How do students reconcile their real-life measurements with the constraints of the page? What units do students use for measuring? How are students grappling with issues of scale? Remind them of the two ways they did scale drawings of the door in Lesson 10; either approach is valid here.

Solve perimeter, area, and measurement problems

Do students use what they know about rectangles to find the area of irregularly shaped architectural features?

In Task 1 of *Activity 2*, assess students' confidence. Are they checking against their intuitive sense of size? What benchmarks do students call upon to estimate size?

Can students apply what they have learned to an unfamiliar problem? Often students are stymied when they confront word problems and have to make sense of an unfamiliar context. Listen to whether students' comments reveal that they match area with the surface, and perimeter with the distance around.

In Task 2 of *Activity 2*, students compare the size of two doors. A valid comparison could be made using dimensions, perimeter, or area. Without supplying the terms for them, help students articulate their basis for comparison.

In Task 3 of *Activity 2*, students use information about area of rooms in the house, as shown in the floor plan, as well as the area of the house—large rectangle—to find areas of related rectangles. They also compare areas using different measurements: square feet and square yards.

Note whether students are labeling solutions with the appropriate unit. When converting among units, are students using an operation that makes sense?

WHAT TO LOOK FOR IN *INTERIM ASSESSMENT 2: A FRESH LOOK*	WHO STANDS OUT? (LIST STUDENTS' INITIALS)			NOTES FOR NEXT STEPS
	STRONG	ADEQUATE	NEEDS WORK	
Concept Development • Draws to scale • Includes amount of material needed • Makes reasonable cost estimate • Confirms cost from a store or Web site • Distinguishes area from perimeter • Recalls the steps for finding area and perimeter • Estimates length using inches, feet, and yards • Finds area using square units • Chooses an appropriate method for converting among units				
Expressive Capacity • Articulates a plan • Explains how the amount of material was arrived at and how the cost was determined • Clearly labels drawings • Describes steps for solving problems				
Use of Tools • Uses measuring tools with accuracy • Uses calculators • Measures accurately				

Notice students' strategies for solving problems that require attention to numerical amounts, operations, and practical constraints.

Teacher: "Why did you need the area?"

Student 1: "We're trying to put tiles on the floor. We had to measure it in rectangles. We multiplied all the feet into inches. Then we added our inches, right? This is what we came up with."

Student 2: "We 'timesed' those."

Teacher: "So when you wanted area, you multiplied."

Student 2: "Another way was [there are] 12 inches in a foot, so [for this side] we did 12 x 6 and [added 8", and] we came up with 80 inches. And we did it over here again."

Teacher: "How did you get it back to square feet?"

Student 1: "Divided 46,944 by 144. That's how we came to this number, 326."

Student 3: "Each square foot of tile is 144 [sq. in.]."

The teacher soon turned to the small group assigned to molding.

Student 5: "First, if you put in the molding, you have to measure the wall from corner to corner to know how many feet you have. We added the leftover on and we got 68 feet."

Teacher: "Then what next?"

Student 4: "Purchase the stuff we need. You always have to have a little extra. We bought 10, enough to not have to go back."

Teacher: "How did you know 10?"

Student 5: "We added it up."

Student 1: "Added what up? How did you add it up?"

Teacher: "Sixty-eight feet is the total. You're telling us we need 10 segments. How did you decide you needed 10?"

Student 2: "You divide it."

Student 6: "No, you add it."

Student 4: "Because 8 x 8 is 64, then we added... I don't know."

Teacher: "I noticed Graham had this great way of doing it. He looked at the 68 and said, 'Well, each piece comes in 8 feet, so let me take away 8 feet; that gives me 60. That's one. Then I take away another 8 feet. That's two.' There was a way to subtract to do it. Meanwhile, Graciela said, "Each piece is 8 feet; let me go 8 into 68." (She divided it). There was no adding at that point."

continued on next page

continued from previous page

Student 6: "How many 8's fit into 68? Eight, isn't it?"

Teacher: "So then you divided, and you came to 10. Why?"

Student 6: "Before it was 8, but we added 2 more on."

Teacher: "So you needed at least one more to cover the leftover, and then you went and got another one, just in case."

Martha Gray
Dimock Community Health Center, Roxbury, MA

11

Filling the Room

How much will fit in here?

Synopsis

Students move from considering two-dimensional to three-dimensional space in this first of three lessons on volume.

1. Small groups or student pairs grapple with the question of how many file boxes would fit inside their classroom and discuss the need for considering the room's length, width, and height.

2. Students share how they found the number of file boxes that would fill the room.

3. The term "volume" is introduced and defined *after* the activity.

Objectives

- Describe a method for finding the capacity of a rectangular solid
- Determine the three dimensions considered in finding volume of a rectangular solid: length, width, and height

Materials/Prep

- Markers
- Newsprint
- Several sample file boxes (or large, empty paper boxes—ideally all the same size)
- Tape
- Optional: calculators, meter strips, rulers, and yardsticks

Opening Discussion

Connect the lesson to the *Fresh Look* sessions.

💬 **Suppose you decided to use this room for storage. What might you want to consider?**

After a few comments, explain that businesses and schools often have to store records, sometimes for up to 10 years, so lots of boxes would be needed.

Display a large box. Continue by asking:

💬 **If you were in charge of gathering all the various file boxes and fitting as many as possible into this room, how many boxes of this size do you think could fit?**

💬 **How would you figure that out?**

Take a few estimates and comments from the class and then pair or group students.

 ## Activity: Filling the Room

Heads Up!

Students may gravitate to measuring and then using their calculators to arrive at a total. Although that method might seem more efficient, encourage students to begin by stacking the boxes. Measurement and calculations (multiplication or division) can follow naturally.

Review directions in *Student Book*, p. 116. Tell groups or pairs that they will have about 15–20 minutes to develop a plan and solve the problem. They will write up on newsprint their plan and the steps they took to solve the problem.

Heads Up!

There is more than one right answer to this problem. The reasoning behind the plans and solutions contributes to the realization that whatever the plan, whatever the answer, each group considered length, width, and height. There are also many answers, depending on practical considerations, such as leaving room to walk, to access boxes, and to safely pile the boxes. The total number of boxes is also affected by the way the boxes are laid out.

Some students might plan to measure the room first, some the box. Some might measure the width of the box first, figure how many boxes would fit along the wall, and then think about how many rows would fit across the room. Observe whether students consider the length, width, and height of the box *and* of the room. If students are relying solely on measurements, suggest that they keep the units consistent (e.g., box dimensions and wall dimensions all in inches, all in centimeters, or all in feet).

When groups finish the planning phase, they implement their plans. If the measurements start to confuse them, ask:

How would you tackle this problem if you did not have a ruler or tape measure?

What changes if you keep all measurements in the same unit?

Listen for ideas about how many boxes fit along the length or width of the room, and encourage students to pursue this line of reasoning. Suggest using masking tape to mark off distances if students are struggling.

After students post their solution processes, ask each group:

How did you solve the problem?

Focus on commonalities by posing the question:

What dimensions did you consider to solve the problem?

Focus on differences by asking:

Why did different groups get different totals?

Students are often surprised when they discover the number of boxes that fit into a room. This observation provides an opportunity to discuss the rapid growth of numbers when they are cubed. Open this conversation with a question such as:

How is finding the capacity of the room for file boxes different from finding area and perimeter?

Summary Discussion

Clarify differences between *units* used and *dimensions* measured.

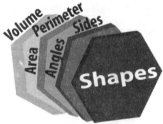

List the three dimensions (length, width, **height**) on the board and summarize by saying:

When you wanted to find how many boxes this room could hold, you considered length, width, and height.

Where do you see some other objects or situations where length, width, and height are involved?

Where will you see examples of volume when you leave the class?

For every situation, ask:

Where do you see the three dimensions?

Derive a class definition of volume. Post this on the class vocabulary sheet.

Heads Up!

One mathematical definition of volume is the amount of space a solid occupies. The class definition may use the words "hold" or "capacity," or define volume in terms of the dimensions involved. Post the class definition.

Close by asking students to reflect on today's activity by writing in the *Reflections* pages in their books, p. 157.

After they are done, ask a volunteer:

 Tell me again, what is volume and what measurements are involved in volume?

 ## Practice

How Many Fit? p. 117
For practice with three dimensional situations similar to the one in class.

Measuring Things, p. 118

Area, Perimeter or Volume?, p. 119
For practice distinguishing area, perimeter, and volume situations.

 ## Extension

Pack It In, p. 120.

Test Practice

Test Practice, p. 121.

 ## Looking Closely

Observe whether students are able to

Describe a method for finding the capacity of a rectangular solid

Can students explain their steps for finding the capacity of the room? Their steps should be applicable to finding the capacity for any rectangular space, such as taking measurements of three dimensions: length, width, and height. They may see multiplication or repeated addition as a strategy for determining the capacity.

The word "capacity" may trigger other associations for students, such as the capacity of a nightclub, auditorium, or elevator. Clarify the word's different uses.

Determine the three dimensions involved in finding volume of a rectangular solid: length, width, and height

Do students measure along three dimensions when trying to figure out how many boxes fit in the room?

In previous lessons, they focused on two-dimensional objects. Now that the focus is on volume, students have to think about adding height to the dimensions of length and width. Watch to see whether students examine the floor area of the room and then move upward to examine how high the space is. If they are having trouble with incorporating height, ask them to point out where they would look if they wanted to find the area or perimeter of the box cover, for instance. Then ask, "What about this?" as you point to the height of the box. It may also help students to use different colored markers to outline the dimensions of the box or to tape out the dimensions of the room.

WHAT TO LOOK FOR IN *LESSON 11*	WHO STANDS OUT? (LIST STUDENTS' INITIALS)			NOTES FOR NEXT STEPS
	STRONG	ADEQUATE	NEEDS WORK	
Concept Development • Formulates a plan for finding the number of boxes that could fit in the room • Adjusts the plan, making changes as needed to arrive at a solution • Notices three dimensions: length, width, and height • Relates the solution to capacity or volume				
Expressive Capacity • Articulates steps or a plan for solving the problem • Uses precise language for dimensions: length, width, and height • Articulates understanding of capacity as having three dimensions: length, width, height • Explains the difference between area and volume				
Use of Tools • Uses the box to measure • Uses a measurement tool: ruler, yardstick, or meter stick				
Background Knowledge • Knows capacity or volume from experience • Knows and applies the volume formula appropriately				

Rationale

Finding out how much a refrigerator, car trunk, or room can hold involves work in three dimensions. Height becomes another dimensional factor as well as length and width, and the resulting volume—which measures capacity—is found. Building a conceptual understanding for that capacity is important; the formula for volume will come later.

Math Background

Many people are familiar with the formula for volume, $V = l \times w \times h$, but do not necessarily understand it on an intuitive level. In counting the number of boxes that would fit inside the room, students build their understanding of volume as the number of units that fit into an area and the number of layers it takes to fill a space.

The activity in this lesson might involve more intricacies than are at first evident. Using measurements *only* to solve this problem might not yield an accurate solution. What sounds like a reasonable strategy— find the volume of the room and the volume of a box, then divide to find how many boxes would fit into the room—may not work. On the surface, this strategy makes sense. However, such abstractions do not take into account partial spaces where boxes would need to be cut to fit. Compare answers gained through each method to find out how widely the solutions differ.

Facilitation

Making the Lesson Easier

Do the exercise as a whole class, talking through ideas before carrying out plans. Keep the activity as physical as possible. Lay out a line of boxes, or pile up a group of them. Model the situation with cubes so students can see the bottom layer of boxes and the subsequent layers building on it.

Making the Lesson Harder

To challenge students who are already familiar with volume, work more closely with the plans the groups devise. Have groups exchange plans and check for measurement accuracy and effectiveness of the strategy outlined. Will placing the box in a certain direction influence the total? Ask each group whether the plan they checked worked, how it might be improved, and how it compares to their own plan.

Suggest that students who are comfortable with measurement, volume, and solving sophisticated problems figure out the problem first using measurements only and then physically modeling the situation. Their solutions will be different, and they can investigate why the number of boxes that fit varies. (See *Math Background.*) Follow up by asking students to

- Find all the ways boxes could be stored in the room, determining which layout maximizes storage space.
- Find the dimensions of a room needed to store x boxes with no space wasted.
- Find the dimensions of the room that would accommodate three times as many boxes with no wasted space.

LESSON 11 IN ACTION

Area functions as a foundation for understanding volume.

Two students were confused by all the measurements they had for length, width, and height of the boxes and the room. They questioned whether to add the numbers or multiply them, though their plan called for multiplying the boxes that would run across the width of the room by the length and height of the room. They were also unsure about what to do with the totals. Finally, the observer asked, "What would you do if you had no tape measure?"

Jared replied that he would stack the boxes to see how many would fit. Asked to draw a picture of what he was envisioning, Jared drew a seven-by-eight grid as an example. Sarah chimed in, "Then we could just multiply the two and get our answer for that layer."

Jared stuck with his simpler numbers. His next drawing helped Sarah see that multiplying the area by the height would give the total number of boxes that would fit in the whole room. Yet Jared had trouble seeing it, so they built a model to help him see how the layers added up. He used his calculator to check that multiplying produced the same total as adding.

In reality, Jared and Sarah had to deal both with harder numbers and with the limitation that they had only two boxes. Their teacher suggested using tape to mark off every two boxes and this worked. They found that 15 boxes fit lengthwise and 13 fit across the room. Using calculators, they figured there would be 195 boxes in the bottom layer. "Then," Sarah said, "there would be stacks nine boxes high, so there would be nine layers of 195 boxes." (She used the calculator.) "One thousand, seven hundred, and fifty-five boxes!"

Patti Vorfeld, observed by Tricia Donovan
Mt. Wachusett Community College, Gardner, MA

Students modeled and understood the problem, but needed more time to make sense of it numerically.

Linda and Ahn start measuring the height of the wall, but they have not settled on a particular unit. Then they use their box over and over to measure the height. They really perfect this when they measure the length of the space. Ahn knows the box is 14 inches long. He holds his thumb at 14 inches on the yard stick and makes a little mark at each 14-inch point across the length of the room. Once they have numbers—eight boxes long, seven boxes high, and five boxes wide—they plan to multiply 8 x 5 and then add 8 x 7 to get the final number of boxes. Time runs out before this group can check its work. Before class resumes and the groups report, the teacher asks Ahn to make a model with cubes using the dimensions of 8 x 5 x 7 to see whether 56 + 40 is the correct number of boxes.

Barbara Goodridge
Lowell Adult Education Center, Lowell, MA

Men often seemed more comfortable with measuring tasks, but in a group everyone has something to contribute.

I brought in four paper boxes. The guys took over. They quickly measured the height of the box—9 inches—and the height of the room—117 inches—and divided to find that 13 boxes could be stacked.

Next they measured the width of the box—1 foot. The room is 28 feet wide, so 28 x 13 will be the number of boxes across the front of the room. Some students were a little confused. I asked them to ask the guys; they explained again what they were doing. Next was the length of the room. They measured it to be 7 yards and 21 inches. They then converted to inches.

Andrea asked, "Why are we measuring some things in inches and some in feet?"

Tim responded, "The box is 18 inches long, that is why!"

That slowed them down a little.

Juan said, "Eighteen inches is the same as a foot and a half."

With that, Andrea said, "That means that for every yard, we can put 2 boxes. In 7 yards, we can place 14 boxes."

Marilyn Moses
Brockton Adult Learning Center, Brockton, MA

12

Cheese Cubes, Anyone?

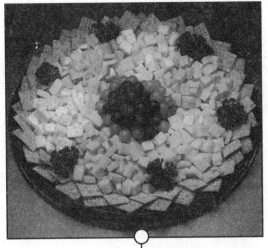

How many cubes of cheese will you need for your party?

Synopsis

Students describe cubic inches of cheese to begin an exploration of standard units of volume.

1. The whole group discusses units of measure: cubic inches and cubic feet.

2. Pairs or groups of students determine the number of cubic inches of cheese contained in a wrapper. They post their data and express the relationship between the dimensions and the volume (the rule for finding volume of a rectangular solid).

3. In pairs, students solve two problems that require measuring volume in cubic inches. The second problem also involves consideration of how dimensions are affected by combining volumes.

4. The whole group reviews solutions to the problems, relating the "layering" of units to area and volume situations.

Objectives

- Demonstrate and explain a cubic inch
- Measure volume using cubic inches
- Compare volumes using cubic inches
- Develop the volume formula

Materials/Prep

- Cheese cut into one-inch cubes. Alternatives include clay or wooden blocks.
- Scissors
- Scotch tape

Make one copy of *Blackline Master 17* for each student to use for constructing one-inch cubes.

Construct extra one-inch cubes to have on hand (*Blackline Master 17*).

Copy cheese wrappers (*Blackline Masters 18–20*), one per student or per student pair. Students can cut, fold, and tape the boxes together during class, or you can do it ahead of time.

Copy Box A and Box B (*Blackline Master 21*), one for each student.

Prepare the following on newsprint for cheese wrappers:

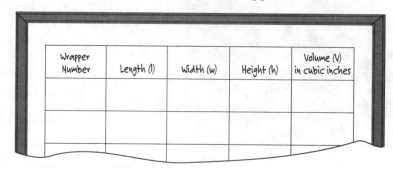

Wrapper Number	Length (l)	Width (w)	Height (h)	Volume (V) in cubic inches

Opening Discussion

Confirm that students match the terms length, width, and height (or depth) in a sensible way with the object being described. If students have measurements of objects from home (*Practice: Measuring Things*, p. 118), they take turns reading their measurements aloud. Other students use their hands to show the dimensional direction and size of the object being described. Alternatively, pass around a box and a ruler, and ask students to show where they would measure length, width, and height. Point out that the dimensions of a refrigerator, for example, may be given as height, width, and depth instead of as length, width, and height.

To introduce **cubic units,** show the class some cheese (or clay or wooden blocks) cut in one-inch cubes, and offer students each a piece.

How would you describe this shape?

Prompt if needed by asking:

What do you notice about the length and width of the sides?

How does this remind you of a die or a pair of dice?

How many faces does it have? How many edges does it have?

What makes something a cube?

Establish the definition of a cube as a six-sided shape with all sides or faces equal. Ask students to point to the six faces of the cube. Then build understanding of cubic units.

The cheese measures one cubic inch. What if it measured one cubic foot? What would that look like? What about one cubic centimeter?

A cubic unit has the same measurement on all edges. In the case of a cubic inch, all edges are one inch. Record a definition of "cubic unit" on the class vocabulary list. Contrast linear and square units of measure with cubic units (e.g., cm and sq. cm; in. and sq. in.; ft. and sq. ft.).

If students begin to see the volume formula emerge from the solution processes, discuss the notation of cubic inches as an inch to the third power (in^3). Explain the exponent by relating it to the three dimensions and showing for one example, for instance, a 5-in. cube, the number of cubic inches in it, then asking students for other size cubes and their volumes. Be sure they record the notation.

Model drawing a cubic foot, and then ask students to draw a cubic inch on their sheets using this method.

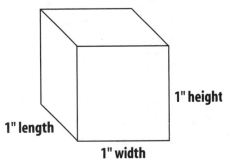

1" height

1" length

1" width

Distribute a **net** for a **cubic inch,** *Blackline Master 17.* Explain that a net is a plan or drawing that, when cut, folded, and taped, results in a three-dimensional object. In this case, the object will be a cube whose dimensions are one inch long by one inch wide by one inch high. Ask students to create their own one-inch cubes.

Heads Up!

Students will see two kinds of nets in the volume lessons. A net for an open box looks like the Red Cross or first aid logo. A closed box adds an extra flap.

 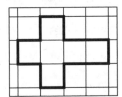

Activity 1: Inside the Wrapper

Assign groups and distribute the cheese wrapper mock-ups (*Blackline Masters 18–20*).

What if I have the wrapper for some cheese, and I want to know how many cubic inches of cheese come in the package?

Students use the one-inch cubes they made to answer the following questions:

How many cubic inches would fill the wrapper?

How can you prove it?

Once students finish, ask volunteers to record in the chart you prepared (or on the board) the *dimension measures* of each group's cheese wrappers and the *number of cubic inches* in each one.

Ask the class:

How can you use the dimensions to find the volume?

How many cubic inches would there be in a wrapper that measures 2″ by 3″ by 4″? How do you know?

Once students articulate the formula, write it in words. Then ask:

Is there another way we could write this to make it shorter?

Write the formula as it commonly appears: $V = lwh$ or $lwh = V$.

Activity 2: Cheese for a Party

Students work in pairs on *Activity 2: Cheese for a Party* (*Student Book*, p. 125). Make available rulers, one-inch grid paper, tape, and unit cubes.

When students finish, discuss each group's solutions. Start with a pair that used a physical method to solve Problem 1 of *Cheese Cubes, Anyone?* (The answer is five bars of cheese.) Ask:

How did you determine the total number of cubic inches in one cheese bar?

How did you determine the number of cheese bars to buy?

Connect the dimensions with both area and volume by emphasizing the layering of cubic units. Create a model if no one did this to solve the problem.

We could mark off the top in square inches, then come down one inch on the sides, and that would be one layer of cubic inches; come down another inch, and that would be a second layer; and so forth. The layers give us the cubic inches in height. Let's see if that always works.

Have students test the formula by sketching and labeling a rectangular solid and asking:

How many cubic inches would there be in a cheese bar that measured four inches by five inches by eight inches?

Move on to *Volume Savings?* Observe who is using concrete models and who is using the volume formula. Ask each to explain their thinking and their steps.

Use the disagreement built into the problem and any disagreement among groups to play out different scenarios. Ask for reasons, backed up with diagrams or models.

💬 **Who disagreed with CJ?**

💬 **How do you think he got those dimension figures?**

💬 **What do you think the real measurements are?**

💬 **How did you figure that out?**

💬 **Did anyone initially agree? What did you discover?**

(CJ multiplied the dimensions by five, forgetting that only one dimension increases when five bars are combined. When stacked one on another, the height increases, or if the bars are laid end to end, the length increases. The size of the wholesale bar of cheese then could be either 3″ x 3″ x 20″ or 15″ x 3″ x 4″ or 3″ x 15″ x 4″; any of these would yield the necessary 180 cubic inches of cheese.)

Ask:

💬 **What do you need to think about when you are combining objects to find the volume?**

Summary Discussion

Review what it means to find the volume of an object or space. Ask:

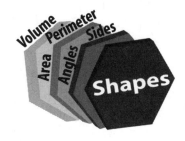

💬 **What do you know about cubic units?**

💬 **What do you know about volume?**

Clarify misconceptions. Encourage students to take time to write in *Reflections* (*Student Book*, p. 157.)

◎ Practice

Pack That Ice Cream, p. 127
For practice finding volumes and seeing volumes combined.

Comparing Volumes, p. 128
For practice finding the number of cubic cm in objects. Note: Distribute copies of box nets from *Blackline Master 21.*

⌀ Extension

A Special Box, p. 130

 **Test Practice**

Test Practice, p. 131

 Looking Closely

Observe whether students are able to

Demonstrate and explain a cubic inch

Students will construct a one-inch cube. Look for them to point out that all three dimensions (*l, w, h*) measure the same in a cube. All dimensions of the cube are the same, so it is difficult to distinguish between the dimensions.

When students look at wrappers, which are *not* cubes (they are rectangular solids), they can begin to distinguish between length and width. Ask, "If this were a flat rectangle, where would length be? Where would width be?" Then point out height. It may also help to draw a rectangular solid and mark the solid's dimensions with different colored pens.

Measure volume using cubic inches

Using the one-inch cube they construct, students will determine how many cubic inches fit inside boxes of different sizes. This exercise will help visual learners; it will also provide a concrete model to those who understand volume, reinforcing the notion of layering to get from area to volume.

Make note of which students use one-inch cubes to replicate the cheese cubes and who relies mostly on numbers, the volume formula, and mental images rather than concrete objects. Also observe which students start by figuring out the number of cubic inches in the cheese block described and which start by determining the number of cheese cubes required to serve everyone (180). Those starting with the block, especially a model of it, may solve the problem in *Activity 2* differently than those using numbers and diagrams (see *Lesson in Action*, p. 144)

Compare volumes using cubic inches

Are students able to compare volumes? Once students can measure volume accurately, comparisons should be relatively simple. Students already know how to compare areas and perimeters; comparing volumes extends these practices into three dimensions. Using the one-inch cubes, the comparisons can be simplified by counting cubes and comparing numbers, much as students counted squares for areas and compared numbers.

Develop the volume formula

After students have had experience counting cubes to fill boxes and have compared volumes using cubic inches, a numerical pattern for finding volume should emerge. Although the concrete activities are a foundation for understanding, in the end students should be able to articulate a generalization for finding the volume of the boxes. Even students who undertake these activities with prior knowledge about the volume formula should gain a deeper understanding from using the manipulatives.

WHAT TO LOOK FOR IN *LESSON 12*	WHO STANDS OUT? (LIST STUDENTS' INITIALS)			NOTES FOR NEXT STEPS
	STRONG	ADEQUATE	NEEDS WORK	
CONCEPT DEVELOPMENT • Finds capacity by filling a space with cubic inches • Uses the volume formula to find capacity of a rectangular solid • Records the answer to volume questions in cubic units • Articulates that volume is area with a third dimension: height				
EXPRESSIVE CAPACITY • Explains the difference in volumes of rectangular solids • Explains finding volume by multiplying length, width, and height • Explains finding volume by multiplying surface area times height				
USE OF TOOLS • Uses a net to construct a one-inch cube				
BACKGROUND KNOWLEDGE • Understands the concept of volume— that it takes up space • Gives examples of volume in real life				

Rationale

Understanding volume both conceptually and through experience with concrete models by seeing how the volume formula is derived will extend students' ability to solve problems related to volume. The open-box model in the activities of this lesson can be filled with one-inch cubes so that the interior of the solid is at least somewhat visible.

Math Background

Students work with physical models of cubic inches to understand the relationship between the volume formula (reinforced in *Lesson 13*) and the reality of a volume measurement situation. Earlier understandings of area come into play, as finding the area of one surface and repeatedly adding "layers" of that area is a more concrete way to see the formula: $l \times w \times h$.

The conventional formula for volume is $V = lwh$, where l = length, w = width, and h = height. This formula can be seen concretely when cubic units are layered inside a box or other container. The first layer total corresponds to $l \times w$. The total for all layers is the first layer, $l \times w$, multiplied by the number of layers or $l \times w \times h$.

Context

Cheese cubes are used in this lesson to allow students to work with real objects in a familiar setting (though admittedly few actually perform such precise calculations to plan for cheese and crackers at a party).

The thickness or height of some commercial cheese bars may measure just over one inch; find a brand that works for you, or trim a bar to suit your needs.

You can extend the lesson and the context by asking questions such as "How many bars would you need if you planned to give each person 12 cheese cubes or 18 cheese cubes?" This type of question builds proportional reasoning as well as provides practice in measuring volume.

Facilitation

Note that there are at least two ways students might approach the *Cheese Cubes, Anyone?* problem. Some might choose to determine first how many cubic inches of cheese they will need for the party; then figure out the number of cubic inches in each cheese bar; and then multiply or divide to determine the number of bars they need to buy. Others might first figure out how many cubic inches are in one cheese bar and how many pieces per person this will yield and then keep adding up until each person receives the requisite number of cubes (nine).

While this lesson does not make it a point to introduce exponential notation, it would not be out of place to do so. Area units are marked like this: 4 ft.^{2}, volume units like this: 4 in.^{3}. For some students the connection of the term "inches cubed" to the use of the exponent 3, connected with the three dimensions, helps make sense of the term "cubed" as used in algebra.

Making the Lesson Easier

After finding the cubic inches in their chunk of cheese, ask students to determine the number of cubic inches in a full bar of cheese measuring approximately 1″ x 3″ x 5″. Then ask how many cubic inches are in a block that measures 2″ x 3″ x 5″. Physically demonstrate the layers of cubic inches by extending length or width by one inch.

Making sense of length, width, and height before moving to volume helped these students.

Students warmed up by measuring three dimensions of a book. Each had a copy, but they did not agree on what edge to measure for the length and height. One student asked, "Does it depend on the direction the book is positioned, standing up or lying flat?" Classmates disagreed about the answer to this question. Then one student wondered aloud: "I'm confused. What are you calling height? With a refrigerator, how do you know what is the length, width, or height?"

The teacher drew the refrigerator and began to label the dimensions, starting with length and width of the door. As she drew, she saw the source of the students' confusion. She highlighted the depth on her sketch and said: "Oh, you might see different words with a refrigerator. Do you know what this part would be called?"

Someone answered: "Depth."

Teacher: "So sometimes it is length, width, and height; sometimes you will have width, height, and depth. The important thing is that there are three dimensions."

The teacher distributed the cheese wrappers and said, "Take a minute to figure out how many cubic inches fit in the wrappers."

Students constructed the wrappers and filled them with their cubic inches.

It took a little while for some students to stack the cubic inches inside the wrapper.

One student had a 5″ x 2″ x 2″ box with 10 cubic inches covering the bottom.

The teacher asked her, "Is it filled?"

Student: "No."

Teacher: "Can I fit more in here?"

Student: "Yes."

Teacher: "How many more?"

Student: "Another layer; another 10."

The class listed the dimensions and volumes of their cheese wrappers.

w	l	h	Volume
3	4	1	12 cu. in.
3	2	2	12 cu. in.
2	5	2	20 cu. in.

continued on next page

continued from previous page

Teacher: "Notice the relationship. Describe the relationship."

Students: "If you multiply the dimensions, you find the volume."

Student: "I love this! Can I write 203?"

The teacher wrote "20 in.^{3}."

Another Student: "It's not 20 x 20 x 20. It's the inches that are cubed."

Students took different approaches to the cheese problem. One multiplied to find that 9 cheese cubes for each of 20 party guests required 180 cheese cubes. She also multiplied the length, width, and height of the cheese bar to find 36 cu. in. Her impulse was to divide 180 by 36, but the answer 5 confused her. "Five what?" she wondered.

When the teacher summarized, she helped students see that five indicated the number of cheese bars needed. Then she traced the method of reasoning Jeremiah used: "If you know there are 36 pieces of cheese in a bar, and 9 pieces will serve one person, each bar serves four people. You need one bar for every four people, or five total." Students understood Jeremiah's way immediately, and they expressed their approval and relief at the manageable numbers.

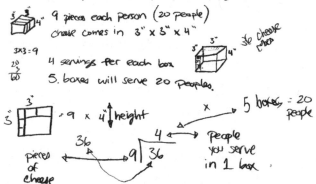

Directions:
- Show all work below. Use extra paper if needed.
- Label all numbers and pictures you use to solve the problem.
- Describe the steps you followed to solve the problem.
- Tell how many blocks of cheese you need to buy. __5 blocks of cheese__

In a conversation about the cheese problems, students pushed each other to visualize many possibilities and reviewed their answers for the dimensions of a bulk block of cheese.

Ariel: "15″ x 3″ x 4″."

Teacher: "What does that give you?"

Ariel: "One hundred and eighty cubic inches."

Teacher: "Does everyone agree with Ariel?"

Dee: "Does the height get bigger?"

Velma: "I think so. The cheese block could be 15″ x 15″ x 20″."

continued on next page

continued from previous page

The class was uneasy with this.

When asked how many cubic inches of cheese this represented, Velma realized she had more than the 180 cubic inches she needed. We all laughed at the idea of how much macaroni and cheese she would be able to make with the leftovers.

Jesus brought the class back to Ariel's dimensions and Dee's question: "It doesn't have to be that shape, does it? What about 6″ x 6″ x 5″?"

The teacher asked the class: "Would he be able to cut 180 pieces? How do you know?"

Dee: "Yeah, length x width x height—6″ x 6″ x 5″ is 180″."

Teacher: "What about Jesus' question: Are there a lot more ways? What do you think?"

They said yes.

Marilyn Moses, observed by Martha Merson
Brockton Adult Learning Center, Brockton, MA

13

On the Surface

How much cardboard did it take to make these boxes?

Synopsis

Students contrast volume and surface area of boxes and generalize about the relationship between box shape and surface area.

1. Students discuss the characteristics of a cubic foot.

2. Groups determine the surface area required for the cheese wrappers.

3. Pairs of students find the dimensions, volume, and surface area of boxes in cubic centimeters and post the information on a class chart.

4. The class discusses two trends that emerge: (1) how the surface areas vary although the volumes are equal and (2) how the dimensions affect the surface area.

5. The class prepares for the *Final Assessment.*

Objectives

- Compare surface areas of boxes that have equal volumes
- Generalize about the relationship between the shape and dimensions of a rectangular box and its surface area

Materials/Prep

- One cubic foot made by overlapping 9″ x 12″ manila envelopes to create six 12″ x 12″ sides and connecting them or by connecting six square-foot tiles
- Cheese wrappers from *Lesson 12* (*Blackline Masters 18–20*)
- Calculators
- Copies of boxes, *Blackline Masters 22–24*

- Scissors
- Tape

Construct several grid-paper, 36-cubic-centimeter boxes of varying dimensions from the nets provided (*Blackline Masters 22–24*); or make enough copies of the nets for pairs to construct their own.

Prepare two copies of the following chart:

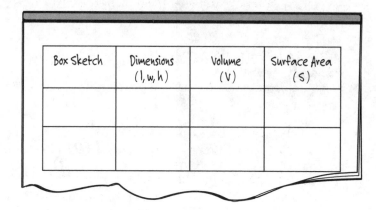

Box Sketch	Dimensions (l, w, h)	Volume (V)	Surface Area (S)

Opening Discussion

Remind students that they worked in cubic inches to solve the cheese problems. In this lesson they will work with other units. Show a cubic foot and ask:

What would I call this shape? (Elicit both "cube" and "cubic foot.")

How many cubic inches do you think fit in this cubic foot: more than 100, less than 100? More than 1,000, less than 1,000?

What would you do to find out?

Do not dwell on the multiplication involved in finding an answer. Students can report their answers later. Instead move on to comparing surface area to volume. Ask:

What would the net look like for a box like this?

What is the area of one side? What is the surface area of all six faces?

Activity 1: Surface Area of a Box

Return to the cheese wrappers.

In the last session, you figured out the volume or the number of cubic inches that fit in various cheese wrappers. Now I am interested in how much cardboard or paper it would take to make those wrappers. This is what we call surface area, the number of square units that cover the solid.

Assign one of the three surface wrappers to each group (*Blackline Masters 18–20*) and review the directions, *On the Surface of a Box* (*Student Book*, p. 134).

Once students have determined the surface area of their wrappers, ask them to post what they found on the class chart listing dimensions, volume, and surface area.

Ask students to explain how they found the surface area. Highlight the strategies students used.

Refer students to the second problem with the 6" x 1"x 3" box. Ask them to explain how knowing the dimensions helped them find the surface area.

Activity 2: Cardboard Needed

In pairs, students determine the volume and surface area of a box of 36 cubic inches.

Distribute boxes from *Blackline Masters 22–24* one per pair, or the net for a box, and ask students to complete *Activity 2: Cardboard Needed (Student Book,* p. 135).

Post the second chart, which also includes columns for dimensions, volume, and surface area. As volunteers fill in the chart with the information on their boxes (as in the example below), remind students to pay attention to the labeling of units.

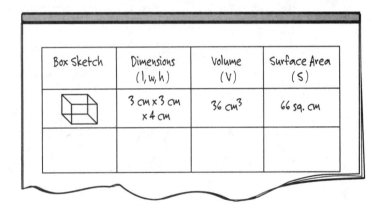

Box Sketch	Dimensions (l, w, h)	Volume (V)	Surface Area (S)
	3 cm x 3 cm x 4 cm	36 cm³	66 sq. cm

Ask:

What do you notice about the volume for the boxes?

What do you notice about the surface area for the boxes?

Ask volunteers to line up the boxes from greatest to least surface area. Say:

These boxes have the same volume but were made with different amounts of cardboard. What do you notice about the shapes of the boxes as the surface area increases and decreases?

Once students observe that some are taller, some are wider, and some are longer, ask:

Which box holds the most?

Which requires the most cardboard to make?

How do you know?

If you were paying for the material to make a 36-cubic-inch box, which shape would you choose?

Then ask students to generalize:

 Describe the trend. What generalization can you make?

- The longer the length of shapes with equal volume, the more surface area they have.

- The more a box resembles a perfect cube, the less surface area it has.

Another option for a 36-cubic-inch box is 36″ x 1″ x 1″. Ask students to predict where in the line-up for surface area this box would fall.

Summary Discussion

To distinguish between surface area and volume, ask:

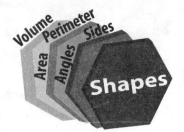

 How are the surface area and the volume different?

Ask students what they want to remember from today, and tell them to record their thoughts in *Reflections* (*Student Book,* p. 158).

Prepare for the upcoming *Final Assessment.* Post the following words, and ask students to share what they recall about each:

Shapes	Angles	Sides
Perimeter	Area	Volume

If students do not mention the following terms, ask about these too:

Parallel	Perpendicular	180°
Similar	Scale	Square feet
Cubic feet	Square inch	Cubic inch
Right angle	Converting measurements	

Practice

Surface Area vs. Volume, p. 136
For practice distinguishing surface area from volume.

Small Box Volumes, p. 137
For practice with the volume formula and comparing volumes.

Vocabulary Review, p. 141

⊘ Extension

Concrete Solutions, p. 143
For practice finding the volume of a combined shape.

Test Practice

Test Practice, p. 144

Looking Closely

Observe whether students are able to

Compare surface areas of boxes with equal volumes

Who has trouble keeping track of the sides of the boxes? Suggest a method for doing this and keeping track of *all* information. Remind students they should have area figures for six sides. Some students may have forgotten the area formula. Ask what other methods might help them find the area.

Generalize about the relationship between the shape and dimensions of a rectangular box and its surface area

Some students will see that the shapes of the boxes are changing as the amount of cardboard or paper needed to make them decreases, but they may not have words to describe that transformation. Ask specific questions: "What is happening to the length/width/height? What can you say about the shape in general?" Note which students have trouble articulating the differences between surface area and volume. Handling models can help students striving to understand how surface area can exceed volume and how equal volumes can yield different surface area figures.

WHAT TO LOOK FOR IN *LESSON 13*	WHO STANDS OUT? (LIST STUDENTS' INITIALS)			NOTES FOR NEXT STEPS
	STRONG	ADEQUATE	NEEDS WORK	
Concept Development • Finds the surface area of boxes by totaling the square inches or square centimeters • Finds the surface area of the boxes using the area formula • Compares different boxes with the same volume				
Expressive Capacity • Articulates the difference between two boxes by noting the different dimensions • Compares surface areas and makes a generalization about the relationship of dimensions to surface area				
Use of Tools • Relies on boxes to determine volume • Relies on nets to determine surface area				
Background Knowledge • Knows about surface area from prior experience • Offers examples of situations outside the classroom that require surface area				

Rationale

Distinguishing between surface area and volume helps solidify the concept of volume. Many students think only about the external faces of a solid when considering the cubic-unit measure. In this lesson, they think about how linear dimensions affect both the shape and the surface area of the three-dimensional solid.

Math Background

While not addressed specifically in this lesson, the issue of units of measure underlies the comparison of surface area and volume. Students find both surface area and volume and then compare these. They find that one exceeds the other; however, they are comparing square and cubic units. Every cubic unit has six faces. When cubic units are combined into a larger shape, some of the faces—and sometimes even entire cubes—can be buried within the shape. However, along the edges each unit cube will always have at least one face exposed; corners will have three faces of the cube exposed. Therefore, square-unit measures for surface area will always exceed cubic-unit measures of volume.

The nets that students use to make their boxes may not all be the same. While the regular, cross-shaped net produces a box, there are alternative nets. If the nets are different, the amount of cardboard used and wasted will also be different. Make note of the nets that students make, especially to confirm that they produce the desired box with its lid (a three-dimensional box).

Making the Lesson Easier

If you feel students need practice with measuring and/or calculating volumes, assign the practice, *Small Box Volumes* (*Student Book*, p. 137); review the practice, and then do *Activities 1* and *2*.

Making the Lesson Harder

Give students the price per square inch of the cardboard for the boxes, and ask them to figure out the cost of making each of the boxes. Tell them to imagine that the cardboard is sold in rectangular sheets. Ask them to find out how much cardboard will be wasted in making each of the boxes and at what cost. They can also figure out which box has the least amount of waste.

In Activity 2, students began to generalize about the connection between the shape and the surface area of a rectangular solid.

After *Activity 2: Cardboard Needed,* the class reviewed their answers. Students calculated the volume and surface area of their boxes and recorded the information on the board.

Teacher: "What's happening? It's interesting."

Student: "All have the same cubic volume. All have different dimensions."

Teacher: "Which do I want to have as a wrapper if I'm a manufacturer?"

Student: "3 x 3 x 4 saves money on packaging."

The teacher lined up the boxes according to their surface area. The smallest was 3″ x 3″ x 4″ with 66 square inches of surface area. "Can you make a generalization?"

Student: "They are getting longer and skinnier."

Teacher: "So in a sentence: If they have more surface area …"

Student: "They are longer and skinnier."

Teacher: "If they have less surface area …"

Student: "They are short and fat."

The teacher pointed to the 3″ x 3″ x 4″ box: "What shape is that?"

Student: "Like a square."

Student: "Like a cube."

Marilyn Moses, observed by Martha Merson
Brockton Adult Learning Center, Brockton, MA

Facilitating Closing the Unit: Design a Box

> **Which box would be best?**

Synopsis

Students do one final construction project, present their work, review the unit, and take a *Final Assessment* test. *Activity 1: Design a Box*, like *Fresh Look*, offers students a hands-on approach to review and apply many of the concepts and skills addressed in this unit. Using the *Final Assessment* as a paper and pencil test is a more traditional way for students to show what they know.

1. Alone or in pairs, students make boxes.

2. Students present their boxes, describing the dimensions, volumes, and surface areas.

3. The class discusses test preparation and test taking and recalls all unit lessons.

4. Students compare their initial and final Mind Maps.

5. Students work on *Final Assessment*.

6. The class reviews answers and compiles a list of favorite geometry and measurement memories.

Objective

- Determine areas of strength and weakness in geometry and measurement

Materials/Prep

- Calculators
- Centimeter and inch rulers
- Copies of *Final Assessment*, one per student, pp. 181
- Grid paper of different sizes and newsprint for students who want to construct boxes to scale
- Shoe boxes
- Small boxes, such as paper-clip boxes

As an alternative to *Final Assessment*, present the students with a homemade object or objects composed of geometric shapes including rectangles, such as a bird house. Ask students to do the following:

- Sketch the shapes.
- Record the dimensions.
- Write the steps to find area and perimeter.
- Calculate area and perimeter of one face.
- Write the steps to find the volume of a rectangular solid.
- Calculate the volume.
- Draw one face of the object twice.
- Do a scale drawing of the same face, where two inches equals 1 cm.

Plan to extend *Closing the Unit* over two sessions.

Opening Discussion

Set the scene by asking:

 Have you ever looked for a box to mail something, but the ones available are either much too big or too small? Today your task is to custom-design a box that is the perfect size.

Activity 1: Design a Box

Students work alone or in pairs to design a box to pack four similar items of their choice. Establish the criteria for success, including the following:

- A box that fits the items snugly—no wasted space.
- A box that is manageable to carry.

Students should record and be prepared to explain to each other the dimensions, volumes, surface area, and reasons for their choices.

Activity 2: Review Session

Transition to this activity by asking students to make observations about their own learning:

In order to complete *Activity 1: Design a Box*, did you use skills that you did not have a few weeks ago?

Build in a review session before giving the *Final Assessment* so students can practice study skills. Say, for example:

One way to prepare for a test is to go over in your mind everything you have learned. List all the lessons we have covered so far.

What do you remember learning how to do?

After brainstorming, direct students to one or more of the sheets designed to guide their review. *Activity 2: Review Session* asks students to revisit the practice sheets in past lessons. Subsequently, direct students to *Reflections* (*Student Book*, p. 159), and ask them to consider what they would put in a portfolio of their best work.

Activity 3: Mind Map

Students record their ideas on the Mind Map for *Geometry and Measurement* in *Activity 3: Make a mind Map* (*Student Book*, p. 148). You may compile a class list with everyone's ideas. Compare these with students' initial Mind Maps, p. 2.

Activity 4: Final Assessment

Review test-taking strategies, such as doing easier tasks first, moving on when stuck for an extended period of time, or thinking back to similar tasks. Remind students to check off the box that best describes how they feel about the tasks (can do, don't know how, not sure) *and* to complete the tasks if they can.

Let students know they can do the tasks in any order. Suggest they do first the tasks they feel sure of; this builds test-taking confidence.

After students have been working for a while, check in with individuals to remind them to check their work. Ask about any tasks they might have marked "don't know how" [to do]. Suggest appropriate tools they might find helpful.

Summary Discussion

Whether or not all have completed the review, ask the class:

Which tasks did you find easy? Why?

Which tasks did you find difficult? Why?

Were there any surprises?

When the class is ready, talk about the tasks and their responses. Encourage demonstrations and diagrams to support verbal explanations.

For closure, ask everyone to mention a favorite moment from this unit or to complete the sentence, "What I will remember about geometry and measurement is …"

Looking Closely

Observe whether students are able to

Determine areas of strength and weakness in geometry and measurement

Can students clearly describe their boxes? Students should be able to identify three dimensions and tell the class the volume, surface area, and how many boxes of a smaller size could fit inside their box. Pay attention to students' reasoning—for example, what considerations dictated the dimensions.

Can students answer the questions on the *Final Assessment* independently? Do they have a realistic sense of their skills? Those who attended class but are having difficulty with tasks might complete the assessment with their books open to trigger recall. If students seem to be struggling, offer them grid paper and encourage them to make sketches. If you notice that some students are working with an incorrect formula, suggest that they show you how the rule works with a simple rectangle on grid paper.

Rationale

Design a Box is an open-ended activity that allows students to bring their creativity and sense of style to resolve a problem. It also enables you to see what skills are now part of students' independent repertoires.

Because the activity requires relatively little new learning but rather is an application of learning from the past several lessons, it is a chance for you to observe how students integrate their learning. They can use each other as resources but should rely on minimal help from you.

Making the Lesson Easier

Be specific about parameters for the box, either designating what is to be packed and its dimensions or establishing a total volume or surface area.

Making the Lesson Harder

Ask students to calculate the cost of making their boxes. Assign a cost per square unit of cardboard, for example, 10¢ per square inch or 1¢ per square centimeter.

The students from the other classes came in, and we got going on the best shape for popcorn boxes. The criteria we considered: Which ones held the most, or were they the same? Which one would sell the best? Which ranked top for eye appeal? Which one was easiest to hold? So. . . Amelia was ready to tackle the cost question on Thursday. She said, "I feel like a CEO!"

Patti Vorfeld
Mt. Wachusett Community College Adult Basic Education, Gardner, MA

Over, Around, and Within: Geometry and Measurement

INITIAL ASSESSMENT

Task 1: Identifying Angles

1. Use your angle demonstrator to identify and record an angle in the classroom.

2. Trace the angle and label it, for example, wall–floor.

Look at each task and decide whether you can do it, don't know how to do it, or are not sure if you can. Check off the appropriate choice, and then complete the task, if you can.

3. Estimate the measure of each angle on the next page and write the number next to the angle.

___ Can do   ___ Don't know how   ___ Not sure

4. Identify each of the angles below as right angle, angle greater than 90°, *or* angle less than 90°.

___ Can do   ___ Don't know how   ___ Not sure

a.

☐ right angle
☐ angle greater than 90° (>90°)
☐ angle less than 90° (<90°)

b.

☐ right angle
☐ angle greater than 90° (>90°)
☐ angle less than 90° (<90°)

c.

☐ right angle
☐ angle greater than 90° (>90°)
☐ angle less than 90° (<90°)

Task 2: Measurement

1. How big is an inch? Draw an inch.

2. Complete the following measurement statements.

a. One foot = ____ inches.

___ Can do   ___ Don't know how   ___ Not sure

b. Three feet = ____ inches.

___ Can do   ___ Don't know how   ___ Not sure

c. One square yard = ____ square feet.

___ Can do   ___ Don't know how   ___ Not sure

Task 3: Shapes and Name

1. Choose *one* of the two cards and follow the directions.

   Draw the shape in the space below.

Card 1	Card 2
Draw a rectangle that measures 2" by 4". On one of the short ends, draw an isosceles triangle.	Draw a square that measures 3" on each side. Find the center of the top edge and draw a line perpendicular to that edge.

2. What is the area of the square or rectangle you drew?

   ___ Can do   ___ Don't know how   ___ Not sure

3. What is the perimeter of the square or rectangle you drew?

   ___ Can do   ___ Don't know how   ___ Not sure

Task 4: Volume

Use the box your teacher gives you to answer the following questions:

1. What would you need to measure to find out how many cubic centimeters a shoe box could hold?

    ___ Can do   ___ Don't know how   ___ Not sure

2. How many paper-clip boxes (2 x 5 x 7 cm) could fit inside a shoebox? Explain how you know.

    ___ Can do   ___ Don't know how   ___ Not sure

EMPower™

INITIAL ASSESSMENT CLASS TALLY

● Task 1, Problems 1 and 2 Notes:

Task	Can Do	Don't Know How	Not Sure	Percent Who Can Do
1. 1				
2				
3				
4a				
4b				
4c				
2. 1				
2a				
2b				
2c				
3. 1				
2				
3				
4. 1				
2				

Notes on Confidence Levels

INITIAL ASSESSMENT CHECKLIST

Use a ✓, ✓+, or ✓– to assess how well students met each skill. When you give feedback to students, note areas in which they did well in addition to areas for improvement.

Use ✓ to show work that is mostly accurate; some details, additional work needed

Use ✓+ to show work that is accurate, complete.

Use ✓– to show work that is inaccurate, incomplete.

Student's Name_____

Task	Skills	Lesson Taught
1. Make an Angle Demonstrator 1 ____ 2 ____ 3 ____ 4a ____ 4b ____ 4c ____	Identifies an angle Records the angle by tracing Estimates the measure of the angle Identifies angles less than or greater than 90°	*Opening the Unit* 2 2 2
2. Measurement 1 ____ 2a ____ 2b ____ 2c ____	Approximates the size of an inch Knows Standard English measurement unit conversions for linear inches, feet and square feet and square yards	8 8, 9
3. Shapes and Names 1 ____ 2 ____ 3 ____	Interprets terminology (e.g., parallel, perpendicular, forms a right angle) Measures and draws accurately Finds the area of a square or rectangle Distinguishes between area and finds perimeter	1 4, 8 6 5
4. Volume 1 ____ 2 ____	Identifies length, width, and height as dimensions for figuring out capacity Explains volume Uses terms such as layers	11 12

EMPower™

OVERALL NOTES

Strengths

_____

_____

_____

_____

Areas for Improvement

_____

_____

_____

_____

Name _____   **Date** _____

Over, Around, and Within: Geometry and Measurement

INTERIM ASSESSMENT 1: SHAPES AND ANGLES

Part 1: Choose a Shape

Use the shape your teacher gives you.

1. Name the shape: _____
2. Trace the shape and color the perimeter.
3. Label and measure the angles.
4. Measure and label the dimensions of the sides.
5. Find the perimeter of the shape.
6. Draw a similar shape (bigger or smaller).

Part 2: Spot the Shapes

Look at the picture of the house. Circle and label any shapes from the list.

rectangle	square
hexagon	octagon
triangle	isosceles triangle
right triangle	equilateral triangle
trapezoid	parallelogram
rhombus	parallel lines
perpendicular lines	

Part 3: Show What You Know

Your teacher will ask you to demonstrate what you know about angles.

Part 4: Problem Solving

1. Fill in the blanks so the report makes sense.

A truck went off the road and hit a utility pole. At first, the pole stood perpendicular to the ground, at (1) _____°. Now the angle is approximately (2)_____° from the ground. The pole will need to be moved about (3) _____ degrees to return to its correct position.

2. The pictures show two cookie cutters (actual size).

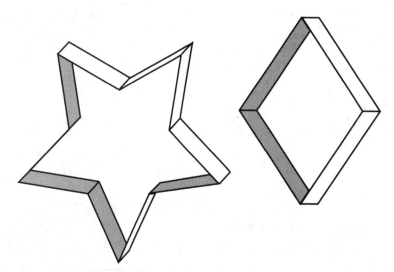

   a. Which cookie has more angles that could break off?

   b. Find the perimeter of each cookie cutter.

c. Imagine that a store is charging $5.00 for the star cookie cutter. That sounds expensive! If it cost only 10¢ for every centimeter of metal, how much would it cost to make the cookie cutter? Show your work.

d. What is the profit per cookie cutter?

3. Maria tried different positions for placing a flag pole on a tree.

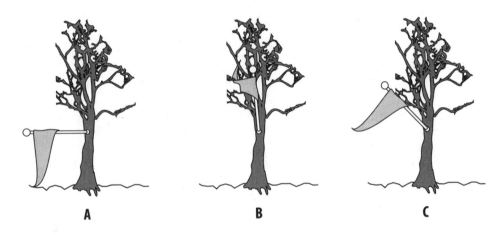

A   B   C

a. When Maria hung the flag with the pole in position A, it hit the ground. How would you describe the angle of the flagpole?

b. She then placed the pole at position B, but the flag got tangled around the tree trunk. Describe the angle of the pole at position B.

c. On her third try she hung the pole halfway between position A and position C. How would you describe the angle of the flagpole at position B?

Over, Around, and Within:
Geometry and Measurement

INTERIM ASSESSMENT 2: A FRESH LOOK

ACTIVITY 1: FIXING UP THE CLASSROOM

Complete the information below to help you get started.

Task: _____

1. What information will you need about the room? Make a list.

2. What tools will you use to get the information? How will you use those tools?

3. How will you record the information so that it is clear to everyone? Make a list.

4. How will you check your work? For example, call or visit a hardware store and ask for their estimate.

TASK 1: FIXING UP THE CLASSROOM—THE WALLS

Prepare a report with a cost estimate for painting the walls of this room. Support your estimate with facts.

Combine teamwork, practical know-how, and your knowledge of geometry to figure out how much material you will need and how much it will cost.

Latex Paint
Coverage
400 – 450 sq. ft.
(37.1– 41.8 sq. meters)
per gallon

$16⁹⁰ gal.

Prepare a Report: Punch-list

The report should include the five following pieces of information:

Check off each one as you complete it.

(1) ___ Scale drawings of the room.

(2) ___ The amount of paint you will need.

(3) ___ The cost estimate.

(4) ___ An explanation and information showing how you arrived at the cost.

(5) ___ Other facts to support your estimate.

TASK 2: FIXING UP THE CLASSROOM—THE FLOOR

Prepare a report with a cost estimate for putting down tiles in this room. Support your estimate with facts.

Combine teamwork, practical know-how, and your knowledge of geometry to figure out what you will need to buy and how much it will cost.

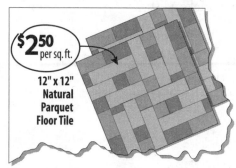

$2⁵⁰ per sq. ft.

**12" x 12"
Natural
Parquet
Floor Tile**

Prepare a Report: Punch-list

The report should include the five following pieces of information:

Check off each one as you complete it.

(1) ___ Scale drawings of the room.

(2) ___ The amount of paint you will need.

(3) ___ The cost estimate.

(4) ___ An explanation and information showing how you arrived at the cost.

(5) ___ Other facts to support your estimate.

TASK 3: FIXING UP THE CLASSROOM—THE CEILING

Prepare a report with a cost estimate for putting crown molding around the ceiling of this room. Support your estimate with facts.

Combine teamwork, practical know-how, and your knowledge of geometry to figure out how much material you will need and how much it will cost.

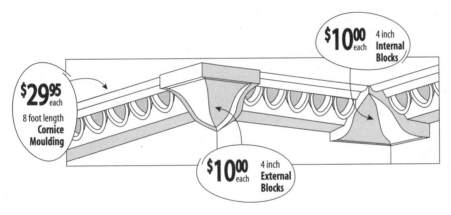

Prepare a Report: Punch-list

The report should include the five following pieces of information:

Check off each one as you complete it.

(1) ___ Scale drawings of the room.

(2) ___ The amount of paint you will need.

(3) ___ The cost estimate.

(4) ___ An explanation and information showing how you arrived at the cost.

(5) ___ Other facts to support your estimate.

ACTIVITY 2: HOME, SWEET HOME

Task 1

_____

Line A

_____

Line B

1. Line A is about how long?

2. Line B is about how long?

3. What are two ways to find the perimeter of a rectangular table?

4. How many square inches are in two-foot square tile?

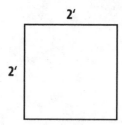

5. How many square-foot tiles are needed to tile an area one yard by one yard?

Task 2

6. The door of Maria's bathroom measures 2 ft. by 6 ft. What is the perimeter of the door in feet?

7. What is the perimeter of the door in inches?

8. How much smaller is Maria's door compared to the classroom door?

9. What are you basing your comparison on?

Task 3

Look at the house plan.

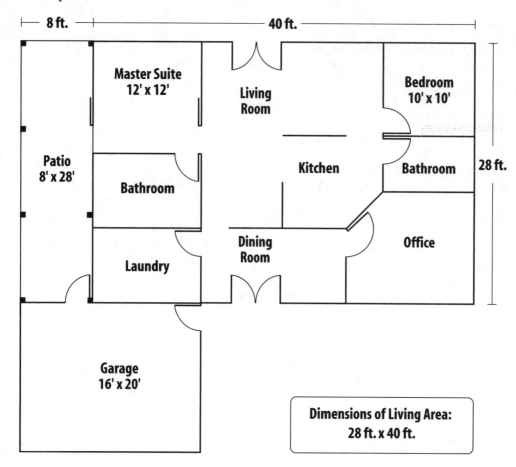

10. To carpet the master suite will require _____ sq. feet of carpet or _____ sq. yards.

11. How much more floor space is in the master suite than in the other bedroom? How do you know?

12. **a.** The garage will be converted into another room. How much area will be added to the living space?

    b. What is the total living space for the floor plan with the added room?

13. Lola wants to buy mini-blinds for the dining room. There are three windows in the dining room. Each measures 31″ by 64″. What is the total cost for the mini-blinds? (See ad)

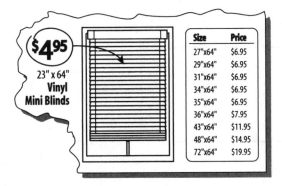

Test Practice

14. The Carson Public Works Department is re-paving the development's parking lot, except the median strip where trees are planted. What is the area of the surface they will be re-paving?

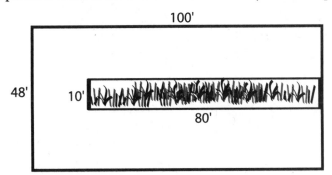

(1) 320 sq. ft

(2) 4,000 ft.

(3) 4,000 sq. ft.

(4) 4,800 ft.

(5) 4,800 sq. ft.

15. Sharon is remodeling her kitchen. Her new counters will have Formica® on the work surface. Before she places the order, Sharon measures. How much Formica does she need?

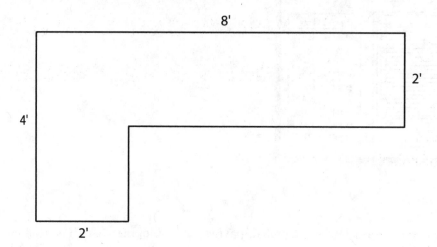

(1) 20 feet

(2) 20 square feet

(3) 24 feet

(4) 24 square feet

(5) 32 square feet

Over, Around, and Within: Geometry and Measurement

FINAL ASSESSMENT

TASKS 1–5

For Tasks 1–5, look at each task and decide whether you can do it, don't know how to do it, or are not sure if you can. Check off the appropriate choice, and then complete the task if you can.

Task 1: Shape Names, Angles, Perimeter

Donna wants to make a border around her tree so she does not have to mow under it. Look at the three designs she has created. The scale is 1 cm = 10 ft., and the length of all the sides is the same.

___ Can do   ___ Don't know how   ___ Not sure

1.a. Shape name:_____

   b. Label angles with approximate measure.

   c. Actual length of each side:_____

   d. Estimate the amount of wood needed to make a border around the tree:_____

2.a. Shape name:_____

   b. Label angles with approximate measure.

   c. Actual length of each side:_____

   d. Estimate the amount of wood needed to make a border around the tree:_____

3.a. Shape name:_____

   b. Label angles with approximate measure.

   c. Actual length of each side:_____

   d. Estimate the amount of wood needed to make a border around the tree:_____

Task 2: Area and Perimeter

Refer to the floor plan to answer Problems 1 and 2.

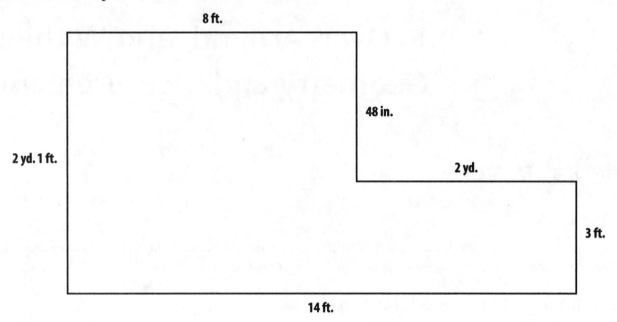

1. Six students measured the classroom. They reported the perimeter in three ways: inches, feet, and yards. Find the total perimeter.

    a. Perimeter = _____ inches.

        ___ Can do   ___ Don't know how   ___ Not sure

    b. Perimeter = _____ feet.

        ___ Can do   ___ Don't know how   ___ Not sure

    c. Perimeter = _____ yards.

        ___ Can do   ___ Don't know how   ___ Not sure

2. How many square-foot floor tiles would be needed to cover the floor of this classroom?

    ___ Can do   ___ Don't know how   ___ Not sure

Task 3: Volume

Refer to the box your teacher gives you for the questions below:

1. Sketch the box

    ___ Can do   ___ Don't know how   ___ Not sure.

2. Label the dimensions.

    ___ Can do   ___ Don't know how   ___ Not sure

3. What is the volume?

    ___ Can do   ___ Don't know how   ___ Not sure

4. How many paper-clip boxes (2 x 5 x 7 cm) could fit inside the box? Explain how you know.

    ___ Can do   ___ Don't know how   ___ Not sure

Task 4: Area to Scale

Four friends plan to share a 60′ x 80′ garden.

1. Sketch the garden's shape.

   ___ Can do   ___ Don't know how   ___ Not sure

2. Draw it to scale on grid paper.

   ___ Can do   ___ Don't know how   ___ Not sure

3. What scale did you choose?

   ___ Can do   ___ Don't know how   ___ Not sure

4. Show *two* ways the friends could divide the garden and each have an equal amount of space for growing food and flowers.

   ___ Can do   ___ Don't know how   ___ Not sure

5. What would be the size of each plot in square feet?

   ___ Can do   ___ Don't know how   ___ Not sure

Task 5: Test Type

1. In the triangle below, what is the measure of angle D?

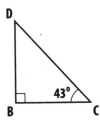

___ Can do   ___ Don't know how   ___ Not sure

(1) 47°

(2) 133°

(3) 137°

(4) 147°

(5) 180°

2. Two farmers measure the height of their corn stalks. Jean says, "Mine are 75 inches tall." Eva says hers are 7′ tall. What is the difference in the height of the corn stalks?

___ Can do   ___ Don't know how   ___ Not sure

(1) 5″

(2) 9″

(3) 68 inches

(4) 9 feet

(5) 159 inches

3. Marta has decided to paint two walls in her bedroom and to wallpaper the other two. How many cans of paint will she need for both walls if one can covers 100 square feet? (Each wall resembles the drawing below.)

___ Can do ___ Don't know how ___ Not sure

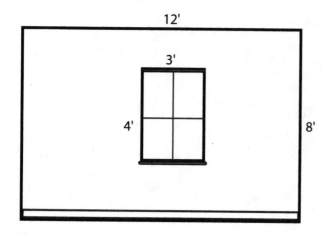

(1) 1 can

(2) 2 cans

(3) 3 cans

(4) 4 cans

(5) 10 cans

Questions 4 and 5 refer to the table below.

	Length	Width	Height	Area	Perimeter	Volume
Rectangle 1	8"			40 sq. in.		
Box 2	4"	3"	1"			

4. The perimeter of Rectangle 1 is:

___ Can do ___ Don't know how ___ Not sure

(1) 16 in.

(2) 26 in.

(3) 32 in.

(4) 48 in.

(5) 53 in.

5. The volume of Box 2:

___ Can do ___ Don't know how ___ Not sure

(1) 8 in.

(2) 8 sq. in.

(3) 8 cu. in.

(4) 12 cu. in.

(5) 16 cu. in.

6. The surface area of a 2 x 15 x 1 box that holds 30 cubic inches:

___ Can do ___ Don't know how ___ Not sure

(1) 30 sq. in.

(2) 64 sq. in.

(3) 90 sq. in.

(4) 94 sq. in.

(5) 96 sq. in.

FINAL ASSESSMENT CHECKLIST

Use a ✓, ✓+, or ✓– to assess how well students met each skill. When you give feedback to students, note areas in which they did well in addition to areas for improvement.

Use ✓ to show work that is mostly accurate; some details, additional work needed.

Use ✓+ to show work that is accurate, complete.

Use ✓– to show work that is inaccurate, incomplete.

Student's Name_____

Task	Skills	Lesson Taught
1. Shapes, Angles, Perimeter 1–3 a _____ b _____ c _____ d _____	 Names the shapes Approximates and labels the angle measures Calculates the length given scale Estimates the perimeter	 1 2, 3 10 4, 6, 7
2. Area and Perimeter 1a _____ 1b _____ 1c _____ 2 _____	 Finds perimeter of a composite shape Converts from inches to feet to yards Converts from inches to feet to yards Finds the area of a composite rectangular shape	 7 8 8 7
3. Volume 1 _____ 2 _____ 3 _____ 4 _____	 Draws a 3-D sketch Identifies, measures, and labels three dimensions Calculates the volume Solves a volume problem using a sketch or the ideas of dimensions, number of layers, or the formula.	 12 12 12 12
4. Scale 1 _____ 2 _____ 3 _____ 4 _____ 5 _____	 Sketches a rectangle Draws to scale States scale Divides the rectangle into four equal parts Finds the area for each part	 10 10 10 5 7

EMPower™

5. Test-Type Problems		
1 ____	Finds missing angle measure	3
2 ____	Converts feet to inches	8
3 ____	Finds area, subtracts irrelevant part	6, 7
	Estimates paint needed for double area found	11
	Uses given information to find missing dimension	7
4 ____	Uses given information to find missing dimension, calculates perimeter	7
	Finds volume	12
5 ____	Uses correct units for volume	12
6 ____	Given dimensions of a box, can find surface area	13

OVERALL NOTES

Strengths

_____

_____

_____

_____

_____

_____

_____

Areas for Improvement

_____

_____

_____

_____

_____

_____

_____

_____

_____

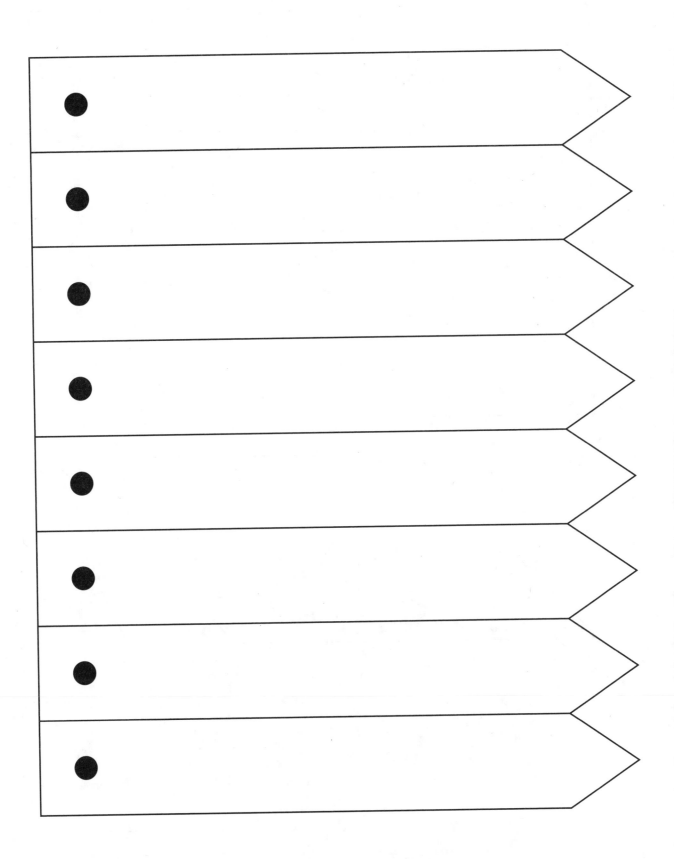

Blackline Master 2: EMPower Shape Set

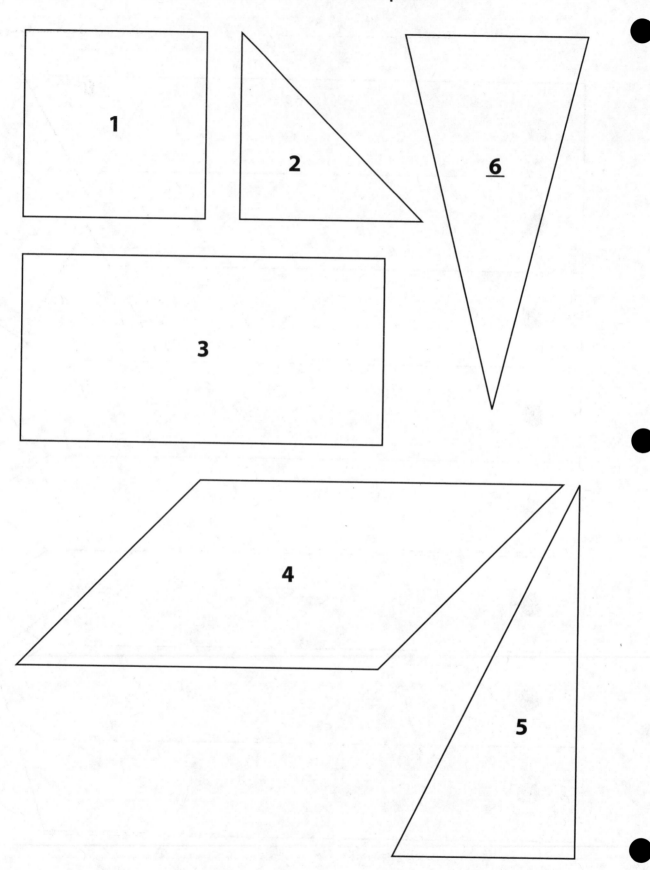

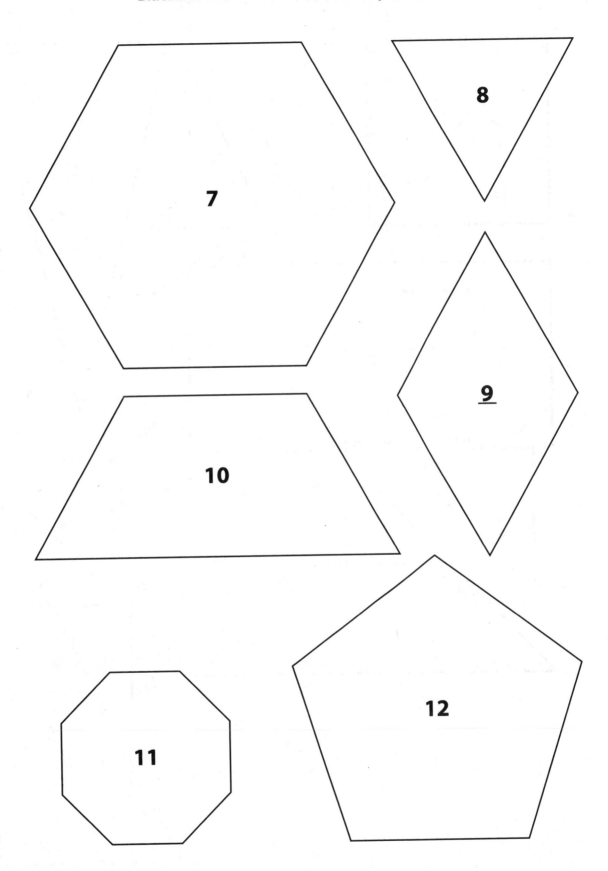

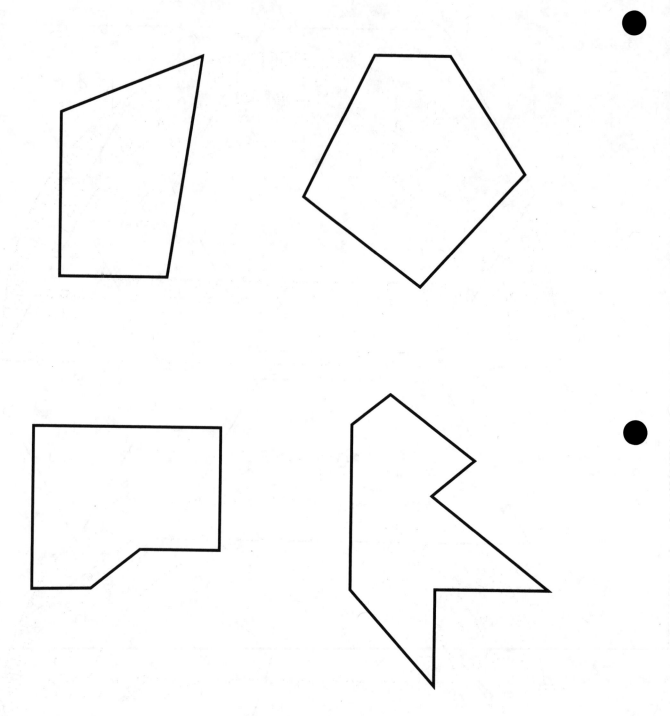

Blackline Master 5: Protractors

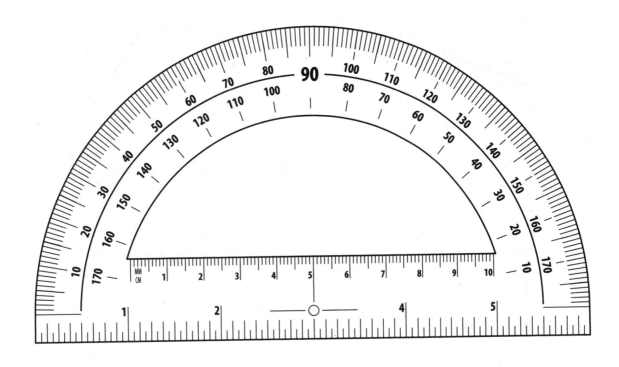

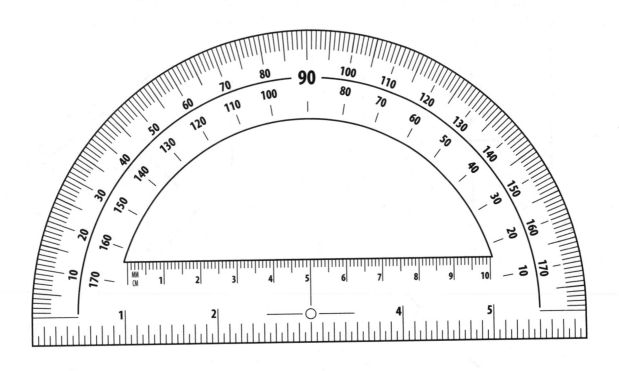

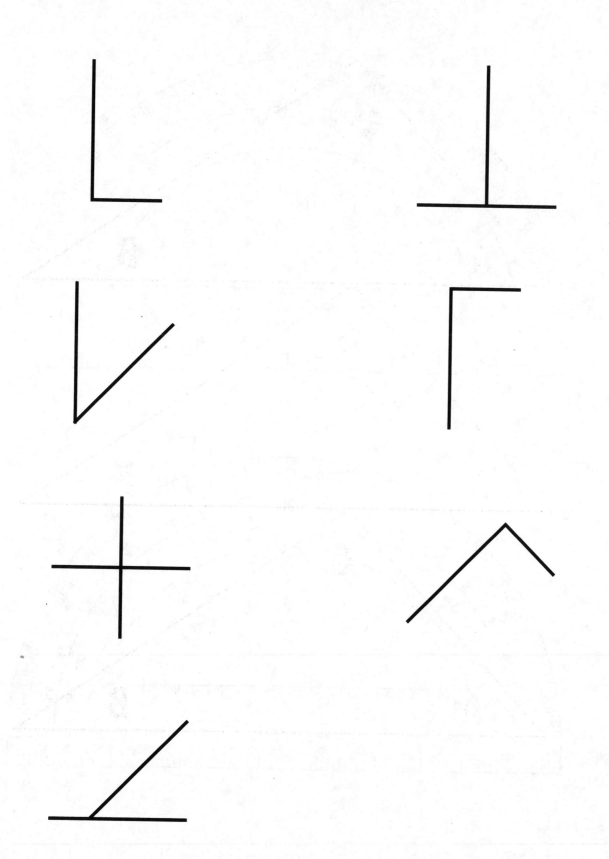

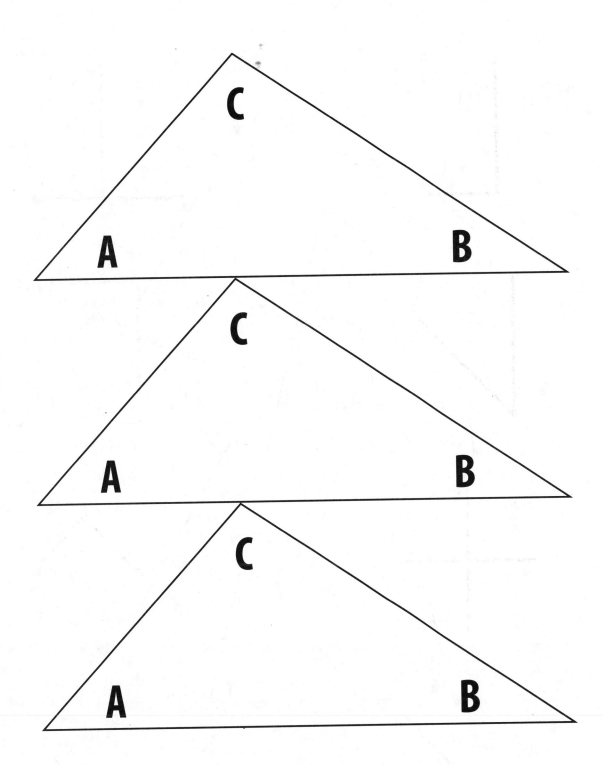

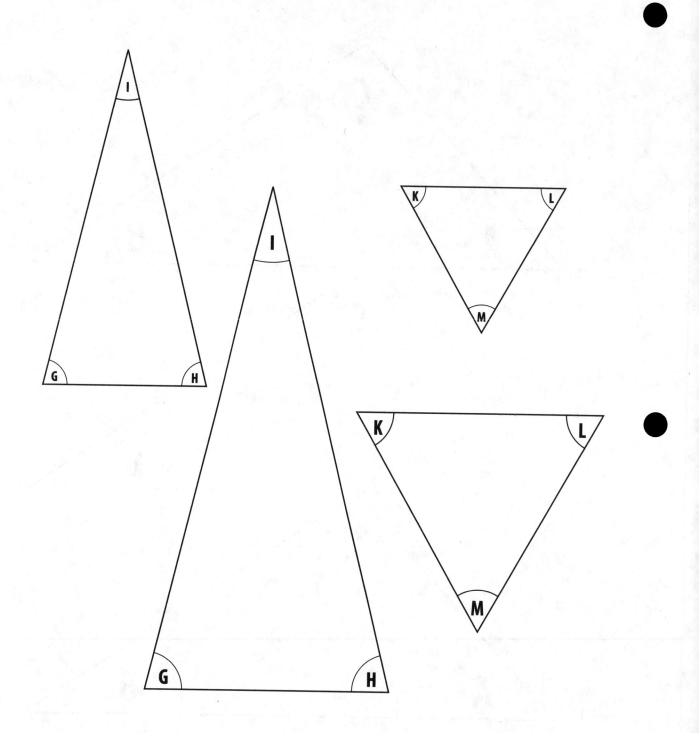

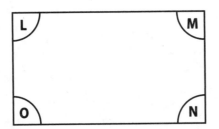

Blackline Master 10: Triangle Types

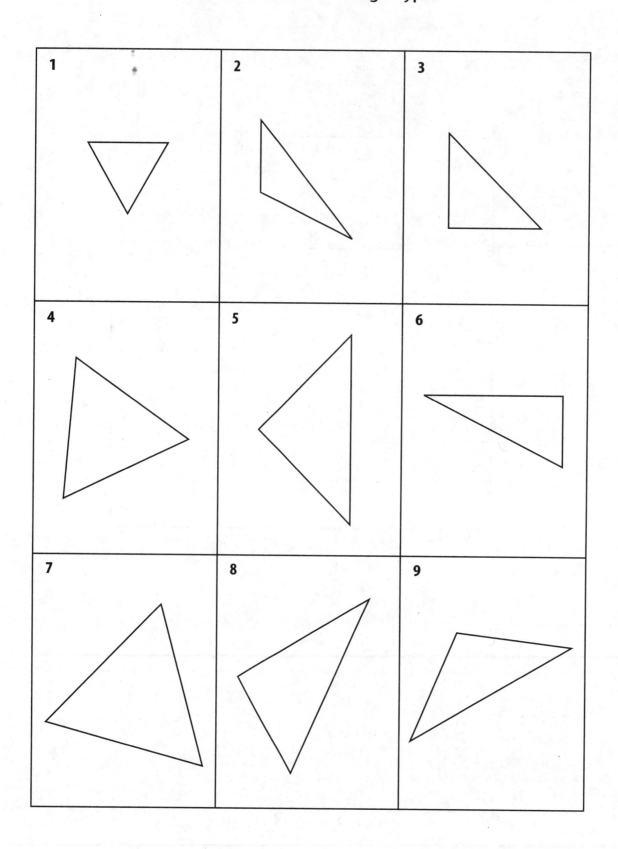

TERC
2067 Massachusetts Avenue
Cambridge, MA 02140
617-547-0430
617-349-3535 (fax)
http://www.terc.edu

Hands-on math and science learning

TERC
2067 Massachusetts Avenue
Cambridge, MA 02140
617-547-0430
617-349-3535 (fax)
http://www.terc.edu

Hands-on math and science learning

TERC
2067 Massachusetts Avenue
Cambridge, MA 02140
617-547-0430
617-349-3535 (fax)
http://www.terc.edu

Hands-on math and science learning

TERC

2067 Massachusetts Avenue

Cambridge, MA 02140

617-547-0430

617-349-3535 (fax)

http://www.terc.edu

Hands-on math and science learning

®

T E R C

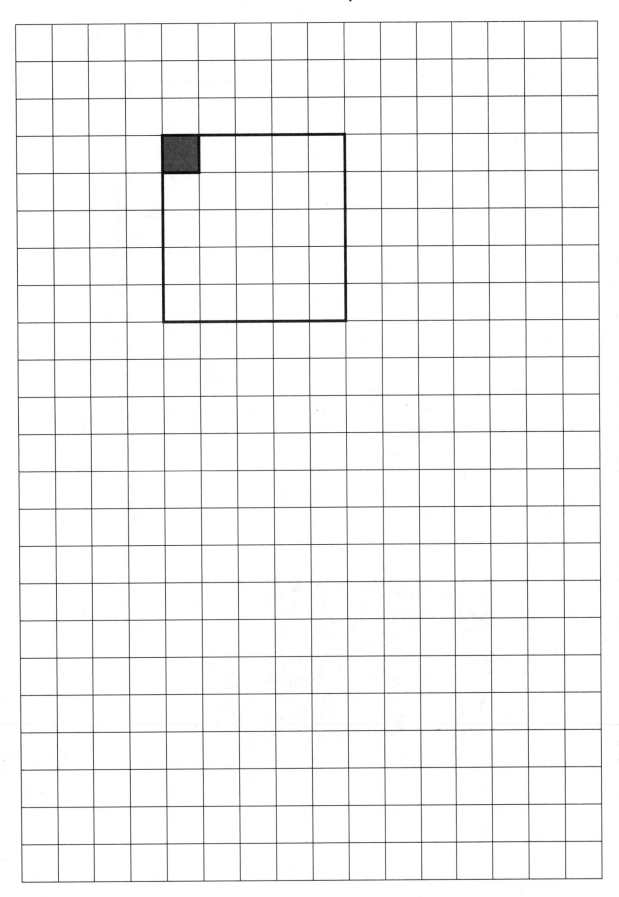

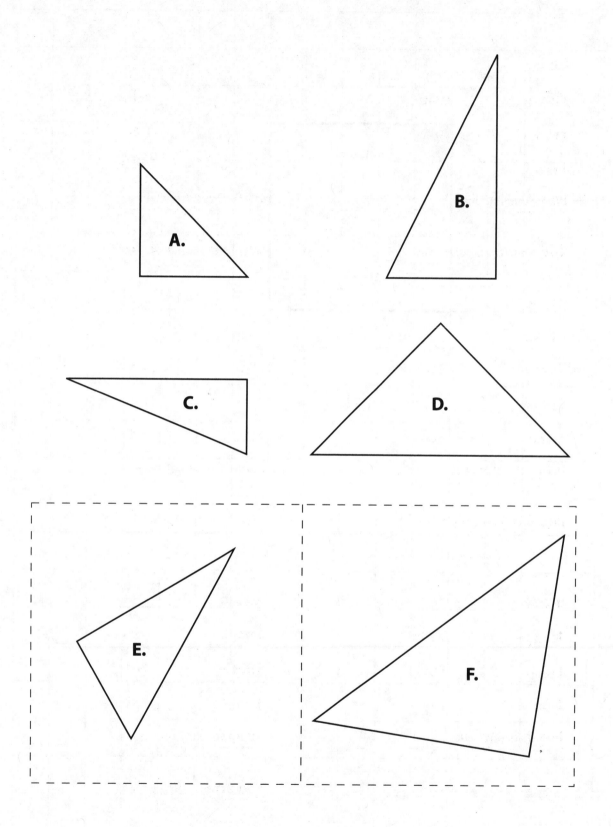

Blackline Master 15: Unit Conversion Quick Assessment

Initials: ______________

1 foot = ________ **inches**

1 yard = ________ **feet**

1 yard = ________ **inches**

Draw a one-inch line:

Draw a one-centimeter line:

Initials: ______________

1 foot = ________ **inches**

1 yard = ________ **feet**

1 yard = ________ **inches**

Draw a one-inch line:

Draw a one-centimeter line:

Initials: ______________

1 foot = ________ **inches**

1 yard = ________ **feet**

1 yard = ________ **inches**

Draw a one-inch line:

Draw a one-centimeter line:

Initials: ______________

1 foot = ________ **inches**

1 yard = ________ **feet**

1 yard = ________ **inches**

Draw a one-inch line:

Draw a one-centimeter line:

Initials: ______________

1 foot = ________ **inches**

1 yard = ________ **feet**

1 yard = ________ **inches**

Draw a one-inch line:

Draw a one-centimeter line:

Initials: ______________

1 foot = ________ **inches**

1 yard = ________ **feet**

1 yard = ________ **inches**

Draw a one-inch line:

Draw a one-centimeter line:

Real Estate

Available in **Dayton, Ohio**

Square Feet: **18,608**

Minimum Lease Rate: **$8.50 per sq. ft.**

Real Estate

Warehouse Storage – **10,000 sq. yd.**
$50 per sq. yd.

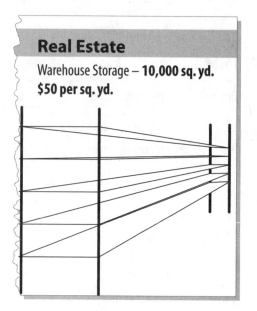

For Sale

Roll of Carpet – **$5.00 per sq. ft.**

Carpet

$2⁰⁰ Per Sq. Ft.
Textured Berber Carpet

For Sale

Roomy Bookcase – 6 shelves
60 sq. in. per shelf

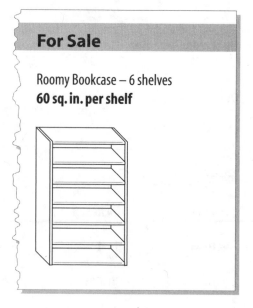

Blackline Master 17: One-Inch Cube Nets

Wrapper #1

Wrapper #2

Wrapper #3

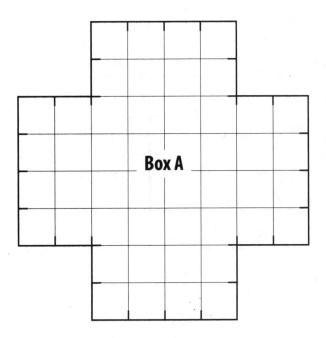

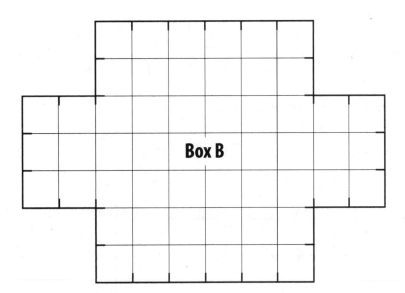

Box C

Box D

Box E

Box F

Box G

Box H

Blackline Master 25: One-Inch Grid Paper

Blackline Master 26: 3/4-Inch Grid Paper

Blackline Master 27: 1/2-Inch Grid Paper

Blackline Master 28: 1/4-Inch Grid Paper

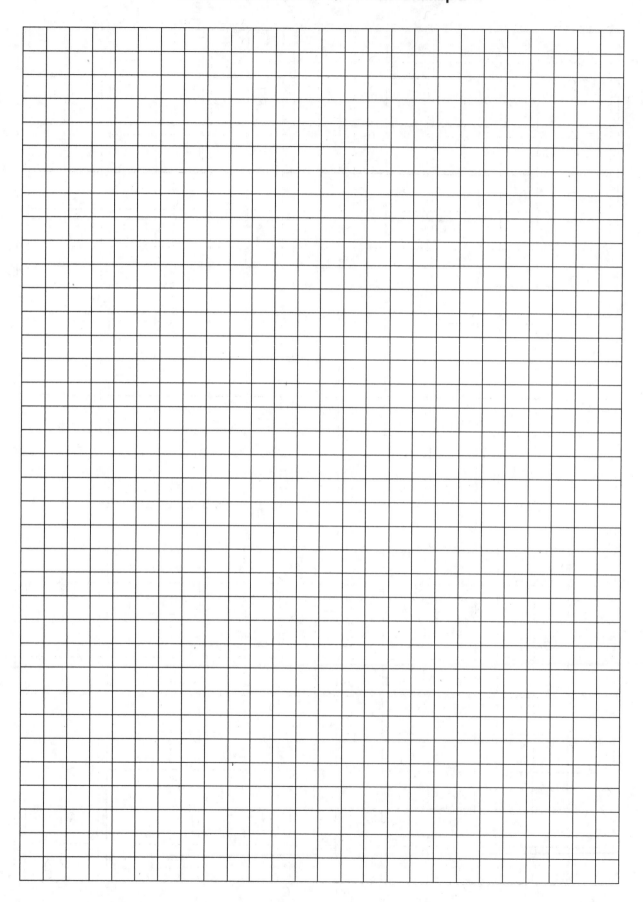

Glossary

Reminder: Students generate their own definitions for terms as they arise in class, using language that makes sense to them. However, to help you guide the discussion, we include mathematical definitions for most of the terms.

Italicized terms are *not* included in the *Student Book* but are included in the *Teacher Book* as background information. The lesson number in which the term first appears is in parentheses following the term.

Acute angle (2)—an angle whose measure is greater than 0 but less than 90 degrees.

Angle (2)—a figure formed by two lines with a common endpoint. Angles represent a "sweep" of the space between the two lines.

Area (5)—the number of square units needed to cover a surface. For example, the area of a 2 in. x 11 in. rectangle is 22 sq. in.

Composite shape (6)—a shape formed by putting together one or more shapes. For example, two rectangles can be made into one longer rectangle as a composite shape.

Convert (8)—to change from one unit of measure to another. For example, to convert from feet to inches, multiply the number of feet by 12.

Corner (1)— the place where perpendicular sides of a shape meet. For example, a rectangle has four corners.

Cubic inch (12)—a traditional unit of volume measuring 1″ x 1″ x 1″, also notated as "cu. in." or "in³."

Cubic unit (12)—a measurement unit for volume consisting of a cube (a regular polyhedron with six faces, all of which are congruent squares) with edges of length one.

Dimensions (5)—the width, length, and height of a two-dimensional or three-dimensional figure or shape.

Equilateral (3)—equal in length.

Equilateral triangle (3)—a triangle whose sides are all equal in length.

Face (12)—a plane surface or side of a three-dimensional object such as a cube or a pyramid. For example, a cube has six faces.

Foot (8)—a measure of length equivalent to 12 inches.

Height (11)—the distance from the base of something to the top. For example, the height of a chair might be 28 in., or an individual's height might be 5 ft. 9 in.

Hexagon (1)—a six-sided polygon; when all its angles and sides are the same, it is called a *regular* hexagon.

Inch (8)—a measure of length equivalent to 2.54 centimeters.

Isosceles triangle (3)—a triangle with two sides of equal length and opposite angles of equal measure.

Length (4)—the longer or longest dimension of an object. Sometimes width and length are interchangeable.

Net (12)—a two-dimensional figure that can be folded to form a three-dimensional figure.

Obtuse angle (2)—an angle whose measure is greater than 90 degrees but less than 180 degrees.

Octagon (1)—an eight-sided polygon.

Parallel lines (1)—lines on a plane that never cross or intersect. Examples of parallel lines include opposite sides of a rectangle and opposite sides of a sheet of paper.

Parallelogram (1)—a four-sided figure with both pairs of opposite sides parallel.

Perimeter (4)—the sum of the lengths of the sides of a many-sided shape. For example, the perimeter of a 2″ by 11″ rectangle is 26 in. Its four sides measure 2 in., 2 in., 11 in., and 11 in.

Perpendicular lines (2)—two lines that form a 90° angle. For example, in a rectangle, two perpendicular lines form a corner.

Polygon (1)—a many-sided geometric shape consisting of lines intersecting at corners. For example, a triangle is a three-sided polygon.

Protractor (2)—a tool used to measure angles.

Rectangle (1)—a four-sided shape with four right (90°) angles.

Rhombus **(1)**—a parallelogram with four equal sides and sometimes one with no angles. Also referred to as a diamond

Right angle (2)—an angle that measures 90 degrees.

Right triangle (3)—a triangle with one right (90°) angle.

Scale (10)—a size change magnitude. For example, a drawing of a desk to scale on 1-cm grid paper might have a scale of 1 cm = 1 foot.

Scalene triangle (3)—a triangle whose sides are all different in length.

Sides (1)—the lines that form the shape. For example, a rectangle has four sides.

Similar shapes (4)—figures that have the same shape but not necessarily the same size. For example, a square with sides of 2 in. is similar to one with sides of 5 in.

Square (1)—a four-sided shape in which all sides and all angles are equal. Each angle in a square measures 90 degrees.

Square centimeter (6)—a measurement unit used for area, measuring 1 cm by 1 cm.

Square foot (9)—a measurement unit used for area measuring 1 ft. by 1 ft.

Square inch (9)—a measurement unit used for area measuring 1 in. by 1 in.

Square yard (9)—a measurement unit used for area measuring 1 yd. by 1 yd.

Straight angle (3)—an angle that measures 180 degrees, forming a line with its sides.

Surface area (13)—the sum of all the areas of all the shapes that cover the surface of an object. For example, the surface area of a cube is the sum of the six squares that cover it. Each square's area is s^2, so the surface area is $6 \times s^2$.

Trapezoid (1)—a four-sided shape that has at least one pair of parallel sides.

Triangle (1)—a three-sided shape with three angles, the sum of whose measures equals 180 degrees.

Volume (11)—the amount of space that a three-dimensional object can hold. For example, the volume of a 3 in. cube is 27 cubic inches.

Width (11)—one of the dimensions of an object. Sometimes length and width are interchangeable.

Yard (8)—a measure of length equivalent to 3 feet, or 36 inches.

Answer Key

Initial Assessment

Task 1: Identifying Angles

1. Answers will vary.
2. Answers will vary.
3. Answers will vary.
4. a. Right angle
   b. Angle less than 90°
   c. Angle greater than 90°

Task 2: Measurement

1. _____
2. a. One foot = <u>12</u> inches
   b. Three feet = <u>36</u> inches
   c. One square yard = <u>9</u> square feet

Task 3: Shapes and Names

Answers will vary. Sample answer for card 1

1.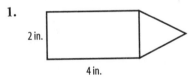

2. Area of the rectangle = <u>8 sq. in.</u>
3. Perimeter of the rectangle = <u>12 sq. in.</u>

Sample answer for card 2

1.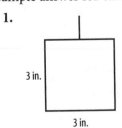

2. Area of the square = <u>9 sq. in.</u>
3. Perimeter of the square = <u>12 sq. in.</u>

Task 4: Volume

1. You would need to know how many centimeters long, high, and wide the box is.
2. Find out how many small boxes fit along the length and across the width, then multiply these numbers, forming the first layer. Then, find out how many layers stack up, and multiply by that number to find the result.

Lesson 1: Sharing Secret Designs

Activity 1: Guess My Shape

See *Looking Closely* for one sample response.

Answers will vary. Sample response:

1. Floor tiles
   4 equal sides; 4 right angles; Square
2. Brace for shelving
   3 sides, 2 of them equal length; 3 angles, 1 of them a right angle; (Isosceles) Right triangle
3. Ceiling tiles; table top
   4 sides, each pair of sides parallel; 4 right angles; Rectangle
4. Kite
   4 sides, each pair of sides parallel and the same length; 4 angles, none of them right angles; Parallelogram or rhombus
5. Ramp
   3 sides; 3 angles, 1 of them a right angle; Right triangle
6. Pennant
   3 sides, 2 of them the same length; 3 angles, none of them a right angle; (Isosceles) Triangle
7. Patio tiles
   6 equal sides; 6 angles; Hexagon
8. Yield sign
   3 equal sides; 3 equal angles; (Equilateral) Triangle

9. Baseball field
   4 sides of equal length; 4 angles, none of them right angles
   Parallelogram or rhombus

10. Picnic table
    4 sides, with only one pair being parallel; 4 angles, none of them right angles
    Trapezoid

11. Stop sign
    8 equal sides; 8 equal angles
    Octagon

12. Pentagon in Washington, DC
    5 equal sides; 5 equal angles
    Pentagon

Activity 2: Sharing Secret Designs

Answers will vary. See *Lesson 1 Commentary* for sample student work.

Practice: Road Signs Match

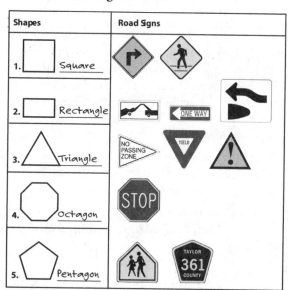

1. E, D
2. A, B, K
3. C, G, I
4. F
5. H, J

Practice: Alike Yet Different

1. Answers will vary. Responses may be similar to the following:

   Both shapes have 4 sides and 4 angles.

   Both shapes have pairs of sides that are parallel.

2. Answers will vary. Responses may be similar to the following:

   The shape on the left does not have right angles, whereas the shape on the right does. The shape on the right has sides that are perpendicular to each other.

3. Answers will vary. Responses may be similar to the following:

   The shape on the left has a pair of angles that are less than 90° and a pair that are greater than 90°. In the shape on the right, all four angles are right angles (90° each).

Practice: Covering Hexagons with Pattern Blocks

Answers will vary. Responses may include the following:

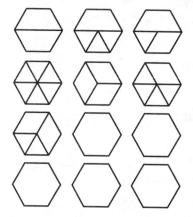

Extension: Hunt for Shapes

Answers will vary.

Test Practice

1. (4)
2. (2)
3. (4)
4. (3)
5. (5)
6. 9

Lesson 2: Get It Right

Activity 1: What Is a Comfortable Angle?

See *Looking Closely* for suggestions on what to observe as students do the activity.

1. Answers will vary. Responses should be similar to the following: As the book was tipped backward, the angle got smaller.

2. Answers will vary.

3. Answers will vary.

4. Answers will vary.

5. Answers will vary.

Practice: Sign on the Line

1. Answers will vary

2. Answers will vary.

3. Answers will vary.

4. Answers will vary.

Practice: Less Than, Greater Than, Equal to 90°

1. a. Right: 90°

    b. Acute: 60°

    c. Obtuse: 120°

    d. Acute: 60°

    e. Right: 90°

    f. Acute: 45°

2. a. 3; some students may see 4 angles, counting the straight angle.

    b.

3. a.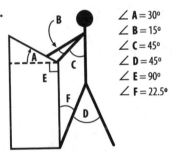

    $\angle$ A = 30°
    $\angle$ B = 15°
    $\angle$ C = 45°
    $\angle$ D = 45°
    $\angle$ E = 90°
    $\angle$ F = 22.5°

    b. Answers will vary. Responses may be similar to the ones above.

    c. $\angle$A = $\angle$30°

4. Answers will vary. Sketches may be similar to the following:

Right Angle

Acute Angle

Obtuse Angle

Practice: Shapes and Angles

1. $\angle$A acute $\angle$A 45°

    $\angle$B acute $\angle$B 45°

    $\angle$C right $\angle$C 90°

2. $\angle$A obtuse $\angle$A 135°

    $\angle$B acute $\angle$B 45°

    $\angle$C obtuse $\angle$C 135°

    $\angle$D acute $\angle$D 45°

3. $\angle$A obtuse $\angle$A 120°

    $\angle$B obtuse $\angle$B 120°

    $\angle$C obtuse $\angle$C 120°

    $\angle$D obtuse $\angle$D 120°

    $\angle$E obtuse $\angle$E 120°

    $\angle$F obtuse $\angle$F 120°

4. $\angle$A obtuse $\angle$A 120°

    $\angle$B obtuse $\angle$B 120°

    $\angle$C acute $\angle$C 60°

    $\angle$D acute $\angle$D 60°

5. Answers may vary. Response may be similar to the following: Opposite angles in shapes 2 (B and D, A and C) had the same measure; the total of the angle measures in shapes 2 and 4 was 360°. The angle measures for Shape 3 were all the same: 120°.

Extension: 90°

1. $\angle$A = 90°

2. $\angle$B = 45°   90 − 45 = 45

3. $\angle$A = 30°   90 − 60 = 30

4. $\angle$B = 40° $\angle$C = 40°   40 + 40 + 10 = 90

5. $\angle$B = 30° $\angle$C = 15°   30 = 2(15);
   30 + 15 + 45 = 90
   $\angle$A = 45°

6. Answers will vary.

7. Answers will vary.

Extension: Degrees of Comfort

1. Answers will vary. A sample answer could be similar to the following: If a tabletop is at an angle, things might slide off of it.

2. Answers will vary.

Test Practice

1. (4)
2. (2)
3. (3)
4. (4)
5. (2)
6. 360

Lesson 3: Get It Straight

Activity 1: Angles in Triangles

See *Activity 1* for details on what to observe while students work.

Activity 2: On the Line

Station 1: Triangles

The sum of the measure of the angles is 180°.

Station 2: Rectangles

The sum of the measure of the angles is 360°.

Station 3: Triangles

The sum of the measure of the angles is 180°.

Station 4: At the X

The sum of the measure of the angles for all four angles is 360°. The sum of any two adjacent angles is 180°.

Station 5: Triangle Types

1. Equilateral
2. Scalene
3. Right and Isosceles
4. Equilateral
5. Isosceles and Right
6. Right and Scalene
7. Equilateral
8. Right and Scalene
9. Isosceles

Practice: Missing Angle Measures

1. a. Right $\angle$ = 90°
   b. Straight $\angle$ = 180°
   c. All $\angle$s in a triangle total = 180°
2. a. $\angle A = 45°$
   $\angle B = 45°$ $45 + 45 = 90$
   $\angle C = 90°$ $45 + 45 + 90 = 180$

b. $\angle A = 20°$
   $\angle B = 10°$
   $\angle C = 150°$ $20 + 10 = 30;$
               $180 - 30 = 150$

c. $\angle A = 30°$
   $\angle B = 60°$ $30 + 60 = 90$
   $\angle C = 90°$ $30 + 60 + 90 = 180$

d. $\angle A = 60°$ $60 + 60 = 120;$
                  $180 - 120 = 60$
   $\angle B = 60°$
   $\angle C = 60°$

3. $\angle A = 45°$ $180 - 90 - 45 = 45$
   $\angle B = 90°$ $180 - 45 - 45 = 90$
   $\angle C = 45°$ $45 + 45 = 90$
   $\angle D = 45°$
   $\angle E = 90°$ $180 - 45 - 45 = 90$
   $\angle F = 45°$ $180 - 90 - 45 = 45$

Practice: Angles and Roads

1. $\angle A = 90°$
   $\angle B = 90°$ $180 - 90 = 90$
   $\angle C = 90°$ $180 - 90 = 90$
   $\angle D = 90°$ $180 - 90 = 90$
2. $\angle A = 135°$ $180 - 45 = 135$
   $\angle B = 45°$ $180 - 135 = 45$
   $\angle C = 135°$ $180 - 45 = 135$
   $\angle D = 45°$
3. $\angle A = 45°$
   $\angle B = 45°$ $90 - 45 = 45$
   $\angle C = 90°$ $180 - 45 - 45 = 90$
   $\angle D = 45°$ $180 - 90 - 45 = 45$
   $\angle E = 45°$ $180 - 90 - 45 = 45$
   $\angle F = 90°$ $180 - 45 - 45 = 90$
4. $\angle A = 45°$ $180 - 90 - 45 = 45$
   $\angle B = 120°$ $180 - 60 = 120$
   $\angle C = 60°$
   $\angle D = 45°$
   $\angle E = 90°$
5. $\angle A = 80°$
   $\angle B = 100°$
   $\angle C = 80°$
   $\angle D = 100°$
   $\angle E = 80°$

∠F = 100°

∠G = 80°

∠H = 100°

6. ∠A = 55°

∠B = 125°

∠C = 55°

∠D = 125°

∠E = 55°

∠F = 125°

∠G = 55°

∠H = 125°

In Problems 5 and 6, opposite angles are the same. Adjacent angles always add up to 180°.

7. Answers will vary.

Practice: Quilted Triangles

Colors students choose for each triangle type will vary.

Triangle Type	Color	Total Number
Equilateral	E	3
Isosceles	I	2
Right	R	5
Scalene	S	8
Isosceles Right	IR	3

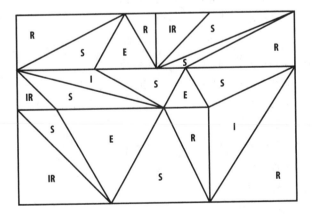

Practice: Measure It Up

A. Right

D. Isosceles Right

B. Equilateral

E. Isosceles

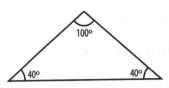

C. Scalene

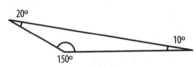

Extension: Hunting for Angles in the Real World

Answers will vary. Sample answers:

90°: the corner of a window pane

180°: where two cabinet doors meet along the bottom shelf

45°: a shelf brace

An angle greater than 90°: a door standing wide open

An angle less than 90°: a flag pole attached to the side of a house

A combination of angles, such as 45° and 90° or 45° and 180°: pavers in a patio

Test Practice

1. (4)

2. (5)

3. (1)

4. (1)

5. (2)

6. 120

Lesson 4: Giant-Size

Activity: Giant-Size

Answers will vary, but should include the correct dimensions. Sample answer:

Name of Item	Dollar bill
Original Shape Dimensions	Length: <u>15.5 cm</u> Width: <u>6.5 cm</u> Perimeter: <u>44 cm</u>
Enlarged How Many Times?	6
Similar Shape-Dimensions	Length: <u>93 cm</u> Width: <u>39 cm</u> Perimeter: <u>264 cm</u>

Practice: 2 Times, 5 Times, 10 Times

1. 2 times: <u>4 cm</u> <u>6 cm</u> <u>6 cm</u>
    5 times: <u>10 cm</u> <u>15 cm</u> <u>15 cm</u>
    10 times: <u>20 cm</u> <u>30 cm</u> <u>30 cm</u>
2. 2 times: <u>8 cm</u> <u>8 cm</u>
    5 times: <u>20 cm</u> <u>20 cm</u>
    10 times: <u>40 cm</u> <u>40 cm</u>
3. 2 times: <u>2 cm</u> <u>10 cm</u>
    5 times: <u>5 cm</u> <u>25 cm</u>
    10 times: <u>10 cm</u> <u>50 cm</u>

Practice: Similar? True or False?

1. a. True
    b. False. The perimeter would be 60 cm because 10 cm + 10 cm + 20 cm + 20 cm = 60 cm.
    c. False. The length would be 5 times longer than 2 cm, which is 10 cm.
2. a. True
    b. True
    c. True
3. a. True
    b. True
    c. True
4. a. False. You could double the size and have measurements of 6 cm by 8 cm by 10 cm.
    b. False. You could triple the size and have measurements of 9 cm by 12 cm by 15 cm.
    c. False. You could double the size and have measurements of 6 cm by 8 cm by 10 cm.

Practice: Perimeter Problems

Answers will vary. Sample situation: Baseboard around a room

Practice: Similar or Not?

1. Similar. Shape A = 1 cm by 4 cm. Shape B = 3 cm by 12 cm.
2. Similar. Shape A = 2 cm by 2 cm by 2.8 cm. Shape B = 6 cm by 6 cm by 8.4 cm.
3. Similar. Shape A = 3 cm by 8 cm by 8.5 cm. Shape B = 6 cm by 16 cm by 17 cm.
4. Similar. Shape A = 2 cm by 4 cm by 2.2 cm by 2.2 cm. Shape B = 4 cm by 8 cm by 4.4 cm by 4.4 cm.
5. Similar. Shape A = 1.2 cm by 1.6 cm by 2 cm. Shape B = 3.6 cm by 4.8 cm by 6 cm.

Test Practice

1. (1)
2. (2)
3. (3)
4. (4)
5. (5)
6. 2

Interim Assessment 1: Shapes and Angles

Part 1: Choose a Shape
Answers will vary according to the shape students are given.

Part 2: Spot the Shapes

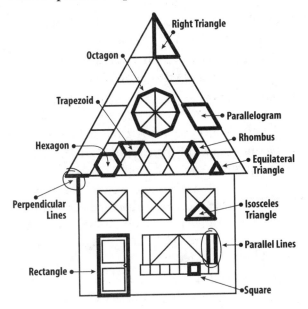

Part 3: Show What You Know
Answers must be demonstrated by student.

Part 4: Problem Solving
1. A truck went off the road and hit a utility pole. At first, the pole stood perpendicular to the ground, at (1) <u>90°</u>. Now the angle is approximately (2) <u>70°</u> from the ground. The pole will need to be moved about (3) <u>20</u> degrees to return to its correct position.

2. **a.** The cookie that has more angles that could break off is on the left—the star. It has 5 interior angles.

   b. The perimeter of the star is 20 cm. The perimeter of the diamond is 12 cm.

   c. It would cost $2.00 to make the star cookie cutter. 20 cm x $0.10 = $2.00.

   d. The profit per cookie cutter would be $3.00. $5.00 − $2.00 = $3.00.

3. **a.** The flag is at a 90° angle to the tree.

   b. The flag is at a 0° angle to the tree.

   c. The flag is at an acute angle to the tree. The angle is about 45°.

Lesson 5: Line Up by Size

Activity 1: Line Up Shapes by Area
See *Activity 1* for detailed response.

Smallest to largest areas:

Shape 2 (12.5 sq. cm)

Shapes 1, 5, and 6 (all have areas of 25 sq. cm)

Shapes 3 and 4 (both have areas of 50 sq. cm)

Activity 2: Line Up Shapes by Perimeter
See *Activity 2* for detailed response.

Smallest to largest perimeters:

Shape 2 ≈ 17 cm

Shape 1 ≈ 20 cm

Shape 6 ≈ 25 cm

Shape 5 ≈ 26 cm

Shape 3 ≈ 30 cm

Shape 4 ≈ 34 cm

Practice: Seeing Perimeter and Area

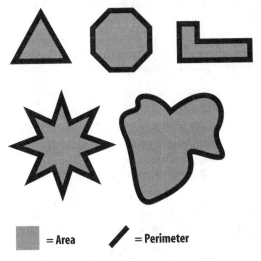

Practice: The Job Demands
1. Answers may vary.

   a. Buy wall-to-wall carpet
   D, A

   b. Put seed down for grass
   D, A

   c. Buy tiles for the roof
   D, A

   d. Buy stone for a walkway
   D, A

   e. Plant trees along a fence
   P

f. Buy an air conditioner for a room
D

g. Find the length of a path around a pond
P

h. Compare the land size of two islands
A

i. Buy tape to put around a window
D, P

j. Do the floor plan for a house
D, A

k. Plan a ride along a river
P

l. Buy a tablecloth
D, A

m. Install a sidewalk
D, A

2. Answers will vary. Sample response: In order to buy wall-to-wall carpet, you must first know the dimensions of the room in order to figure out the square footage because carpet is sold by the square yard.

3. Answers will vary. Sample response: If you wanted to assure that everyone in an office has the same amount of work space, you would find the area of each cubicle.

4. Answers will vary. Sample response: If you want to put new weather stripping around a door or window, you must know the perimeter so you know how much stripping is needed.

Practice: The Caterers' Question

1. Answers will vary but should be similar to the following: If the piece came from Rachel's cake, the person should not be complaining because all the pieces are of equal size. Rachel cut the cake into thirds and then cut each third in half again, creating either two rectangles or two triangles of equal size from each third of the cake.

   If the piece came from Mike's cake, the person who complained about getting a smaller piece may have been correct because Mike did not cut his cake into equally sized pieces.

2. Answers may vary, but each design should be cut into 6 equal pieces. Sample answers:

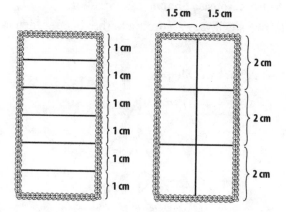

Extension: Area and Perimeter in My Neighborhood

1. Answers will vary. Sample answer: The wood that surrounds my raised garden beds reminds me of a perimeter. It surrounds the garden bed and holds in the soil. It is a rectangular shape 8 feet long and 3 feet wide.

2. Answers will vary. Sample answer: The top of the soil in my raised garden beds reminds me of area. It is the space that I have to plant my garden. It is a rectangular shape 8 feet long and 3 feet wide so the area is about 24 square feet.

3. Answers will vary.

Test Practice

1. (2)
2. (2)
3. (4)
4. (4)
5. (1)
6. 28

Lesson 6: Combining Rectangles

Activity 1: Drawing Four Rectangles

Answers will vary. Sample answer:

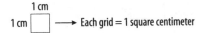

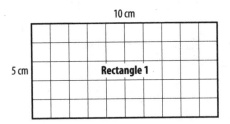

Rectangle 1

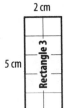

Rectangle 2

Rectangle 3

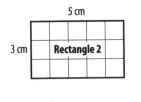

Rectangle 4

	Length (l)	Width (w)	Area (A)	Perimeter (P)
1	10 cm	5 cm	50 sq. cm	30 cm
2	5 cm	3 cm	15 sq. cm	16 cm
3	2 cm	5 cm	10 sq. cm	14 cm
4	3 cm	4 cm	12 sq. cm	14 cm
All Rectangles Combined			87 sq. cm	74 cm

Activity 2: Making a Composite Shape

1. Answers will vary, but the correct prediction is that the area of the combined shape will be the same as the total area of the original four shapes.

2. Answers will vary, but the correct prediction is that the perimeter of the combined shape will be smaller than the total perimeter of the original four shapes.

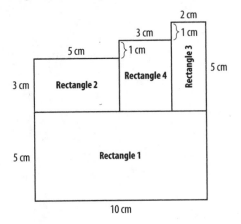

3. The area of the new shape is 87 sq. cm.
4. The perimeter of the new shape is 40 cm.
5. The shape has 8 sides.
6. The shape has 8 angles. All of the angles are 90° angles or 270° angles.

My Composite Shape

Area (A) sq. cm   87 sq. cm
Perimeter (P) cm   40 cm
Number of Angles   10 (including 2 exterior angles)
Number of Sides   10

Practice: Area of 24 Sq. Cm

1. Answers will vary. Sample answer:

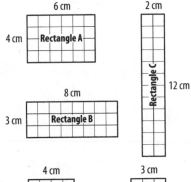

A. $l = 6$ cm

$w = 4$ cm

$6 + 6 + 4 + 4 = 20$ cm

24 sq. cm

B. $l = 8$ cm

$w = 3$ cm

$8 + 8 + 3 + 3 = 22$ cm

24 sq. cm

C. $l = 2$ cm

$w = 12$ cm

$2 + 2 + 12 + 12 = 28$ cm

24 sq. cm

D. $l = 4$ cm

$w = 6$ cm

$4 + 4 + 6 + 6 = 20$ cm

24 sq. cm

E. $l = 3$ cm

$w = 8$ cm

$3 + 3 + 8 + 8 = 22$ cm

24 sq. cm

2. Answers will vary. Answer based on sample above: The rectangle with the smallest perimeter is the one with dimensions of 4 cm by 6 cm. It is shaped more like a square than the other rectangles.

3. Answers will vary. Answer based on sample above: The rectangle with the largest perimeter is the one with dimensions of 2 cm by 12 cm. It is very long and skinny.

Practice: Divide the Shapes

Answers will vary. One possible answer for each is given below:

1. 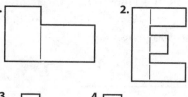 2.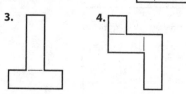

3. 4.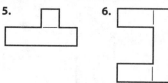

5. 6.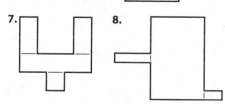

7. 8.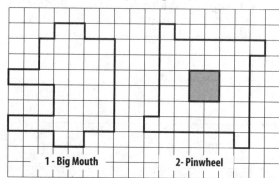

Practice: Cookie Cutter

1. Answers will vary. Sample answer:

Cookie Cutter 1 Area: 36 sq. cm; Perimeter 36 cm

Cookie Cutter 2 Area: 36 sq. cm; Perimeter 40 cm

2. The metalsmith needs to know the perimeter because it describes the length of metal needed for the cookie cutter.

3. Answers will vary. Answer based on sample above: Cookie Cutter 1 would be the cheaper. It would cost $3.60 for the metal.

4. Answers will vary.

5. Answers will vary.

EMPower™

6. Answers will vary. Answer based on sample above: Probably Cookie Cutter 2 is more practical because there are fewer angles to cut (Cookie Cutter 1 has 11 interior and 7 exterior angles; Cookie Cutter 2 has a total of 16 angles: 8 interior, 4 exterior, and 4 exterior [but interior] to the center hole).

Practice: Area in Packaging

Answers will vary. Sample answer:

1. There are approximately 126 sq. cm of cardboard needed to construct the box.

2. Sample answer:

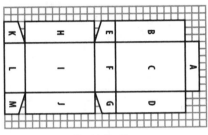

F = **21** (7 x 3)
A = **14** (7 x 2)
L = **21** (7 x 3)
B, C, D = **130** (10 x 13)
H, I, J = **130** (10 x 13)
E, G, K, M = **32** (6 + 2 each)
348 sq. cm

Extension: Sides and Angles

Answers will vary. Sample answer:

1.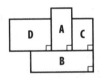

A = 2 x 4
B = 6 x 2
C = 2 x 3
D = 4 x 3

2.

Number of Rectangles	Number of Sides	Number of Angles
2	8	8: 6 interior 2 exterior
3	8	8: 6 interior 2 exterior
4	10	10: 7 interior 3 exterior

3. The number of sides and angles are equal for each composite shape.

4. Answers will vary.

5. All the angles are right angles. This is so because all the shapes used were rectangles, which only have right angles.

6. If a shape had 8 angles, it should also have 8 sides because the number of angles and the number of sides for a shape is always the same.

Test Practice

1. (2)
2. (4)
3. (3)
4. (2)
5. (2)
6. 56

Lesson 7: Disappearing Grid Lines

Activity 1: Missing Measurements

1. Students draw rectangles on sq. cm paper as per the dimensions in the table below.

2.

Shape	Length (l)	Width (w)	Area (A)	Perimeter (P)
1	10 cm	6 cm	60 sq. cm	32 cm
2	12 cm	5 cm	60 sq. cm	34 cm
3	4 cm	3 cm	12 sq. cm	14 cm
4	4 cm	2 cm	8 sq. cm	12 cm
5	16 cm	4 cm	64 sq. cm	40 cm
6	12 cm	2 cm	24 sq. cm	28 cm
7	12 cm	12 cm	144 sq. cm	48 cm
8	18 cm	8 cm	144 sq. cm	52 cm

3. Answers will vary.

Activity 2: When the Grid Lines Disappear

1.

Shape	Length (*l*)	Width (*w*)	Area (*A*)	Perimeter (*P*)
1	3 cm	5 cm	15 sq. cm	16 cm
2	8 cm	10 cm	80 sq. cm	36 cm
3	4 cm	3 cm	12 sq. cm	14 cm
4	4 cm	2 cm	8 sq. cm	12 cm

2. Answers will vary.

Activity 3: Areas of Right Triangles

1. a. 4.5 sq. cm

  b. 9 sq. cm

  c. 5 sq. cm

  d. 12.5 sq. cm

  e. 7.5 sq. cm

  f. 18 sq. cm

2. Two triangles fit inside the square.

3. You can find the area of the *square* by using the following formula: s^2 (or *l w*) = Area

4. To find the area of one triangle you can first figure out the area of the rectangle, then take half of that area.

Practice: Missing Measurements

1. Students draw rectangles on sq. cm paper as per the dimensions in the following table.

2.

	Length (*l*)	Width (*w*)	Area (*A*)	Perimeter (*P*)
1	5 cm	4 cm	20 sq. cm	18 cm
2	10 cm	3 cm	30 sq. cm	26 cm
3	6 cm	4 cm	24 sq. cm	20 cm
4	5 cm	5 cm	15 sq. cm	16 cm
5	30 cm	20 cm	600 sq. cm	100 cm
6	15 cm	2 cm	30 sq. cm	34 cm
7	90 cm	2 cm	180 sq. cm	184 cm
8	45 cm	4 cm	180 sq. cm	98 cm

3. Answers will vary.

Practice: More Complex Shapes

1. a. Sum of the areas of the four rectangles = 32 sq. cm

  b. Area of composite shape = 32 sq. cm

  c. Sum of the perimeters of the four rectangles = 52 cm

  d. Perimeter of composite shape = 34 cm

2. a. Sum of areas = 24 sq. cm

  b. Area of composite shape = 24 sq. cm

  c. Sum of perimeters = 32 cm (if divided into two 2 x 6 shapes); 36 cm (if divided into one 2 x 8 shape and two 2 x 2 shapes)

  d. Perimeter of composite shape = 28 cm

3. a. Sum of areas = 18 sq. cm

  b. Area of composite shape = 18 sq. cm

  c. Sum of perimeters = 26 cm (if divided into a 2 x 6 shape and a 2 x 3 shape); 24 cm (if divided into a 2 x 3 shape and a 3 x 4 shape)

  d. Perimeter of composite shape = 20 cm

4. **a.** Sum of areas = 175 sq. cm

   b. Area of composite shape = 175 sq. cm

   c. Sum of perimeters = 72 cm

   d. Perimeter of composite shape = 62 cm

5. **a.** Sum of areas = 425 sq. cm

   b. Area of composite shape = 425 sq. cm

   c. Sum of perimeters = 140 cm (if divided into three shapes: 5 x 20, 5 x 5, and 15 x 20 or 5 x 15, 10 x 5, and 15 x 20)

   d. Perimeter of composite shape = 120 cm

Practice: Von's Kitchen

1. Area = 120 sq. feet

2. Perimeter = 44 feet

3. Answers will vary. One method might be to multiply the length by the width.

4. Answers will vary. One method might be to draw a picture and count the squares.

5. Answers will vary.

6. Answers will vary. One method might be to multiply both the length and the width by two, then add the two amounts together.

7. Answers will vary. One method might be to add the length and the width together, then multiply the total by two.

8. Answers will vary.

Practice: Areas of More Right Triangles

1. Area of the rectangle <u>1,200 sq. cm</u>
   Area of the triangle <u>600 sq. cm</u>

2. Area of the rectangle <u>5,000 sq. cm</u>
   Area of the triangle <u>2,500 sq. cm</u>

3. Area of the rectangle <u>100 sq. cm</u>
   Area of the triangle <u>50 sq. cm</u>

4. Area of the rectangle <u>4,000 sq. cm</u>
   Area of the triangle <u>2,000 sq. cm</u>

Extension: Area and Perimeter Challenges

1. Students draw squares on sq. cm paper as per the dimensions in the table below.

a.	1 cm by 1 cm	4 cm	1 sq. cm
b.	2 cm by 2 cm	8 cm	4 sq. cm
c.	3 cm by 3 cm	12 cm	9 sq. cm
d.	4 cm by 4 cm	16 cm	16 sq. cm
e.	5 cm by 5 cm	20 cm	25 sq. cm
f.	6 cm by 6 cm	24 cm	36 sq. cm
g.	7 cm by 7 cm	28 cm	49 sq. cm
h.	8 cm by 8 cm	32 cm	64 sq. cm
i.	9 cm by 9 cm	36 cm	81 sq. cm
j.	10 cm by 10 cm	40 cm	100 sq. cm

2. Each time the square grows by one cm on each side, the perimeter grows by 4 cm.

3. Answers will vary. A sample answer: The area of each square is a perfect square. The area changes to the next perfect square every time one cm is added to each side of the square.

4. Answers will vary. A sample answer: For every cm increase in the shape of a square, the perimeter increases by 4 cm.

Test Practice

1. (3)

2. (3)

3. (1)

4. (3)

5. (4)

6. 1,600

Lesson 8: Conversion Experiences

Activity: It's All in How You Measure

1. | | | | |
   |---|---|---|---|
   | 1 | 1.5 feet by 3 feet | 9 feet |
   | 2 | 3 feet by 6 feet | 18 feet |
   | 3 | 6 feet by 9 feet | 30 feet |

2. Answers will vary.

3. | | | | |
   |---|---|---|---|
   | 1 | 108 | 9 | 3 |
   | 2 | 216 | 18 | 6 |
   | 3 | 360 | 30 | 10 |

4. All of the perimeter measurements for Rectangle 1 are equal. Explanations will vary.

5. All of the perimeter measurements for Rectangle 2 are equal. Explanations will vary.

6. All of the perimeter measurements for Rectangle 3 are equal. Explanations will vary.

7. Answers will vary.

8. **a.** 120″ = <u>10</u> feet

   b. 36′ = <u>12</u> yards

   c. 72″ = <u>2</u> yards

   d. 84″ = <u>7</u> feet

   e. 180′ = <u>60</u> yards

   f. 108″ = <u>9</u> feet

Practice: Home Measurements

Answers will vary.

Practice: Units of Measure

Inches, in. *or* "
>   Answers will vary.
>   Sample answer: The length of a joint in my finger

Feet, ft. *or* '
>   Answers will vary.
>   Sample answer: The length of a sheet of paper

Yards, yd.
>   Answers will vary.
>   Sample answer: The width of a regular door frame

Centimeters, cm
>   Answers will vary.
>   Sample answer: The width of my pinkie

Meters, M
>   Answers will vary.
>   Sample answer: Three inches wider than a standard door frame

Practice: Keeping Units Straight

1. **a.** Length in inches = 11
        width in inches = 8.5

    b. Length in centimeters ≈ 28
        width in centimeters ≈ 22.5

2. **a.** Perimeter in inches = 39

    b. Perimeter in centimeters = 101

3. **a.** 1 inch = 2 cm

    b. 6 inches = 15 cm

    c. 1 foot = 12 inches

    d. 3 feet = 36 inches

    e. 6 feet = 72 inches = 180 cm

4. Answers will vary. Sample answers:

    a. 5 feet, 4 inches

    b. 64 inches

    c. About 160 cm

Extension: Conversion Match

1. **a.** 10

    b. 5

    c. 3 and 7

    d. 6

    e. 1

    f. 8

g. 4

h. 9

i. 2

2. **a.** 1 yd. = 36 in.
        3 yd. = 108 in.
        1/2 yd. = 18 in.

    b. 1 mi. = 5,280 ft.
        3 mi. = 15,840 ft.
        1/2 mi. = 2,640 ft.

    c. 1 qt. = 2 pt. or 32 oz.
        3 qt. = 6 pt. or 96 oz.
        1/2 qt. = 1 pt. or 16 oz.

    d. 1 lb. = 16 oz.
        3 lb. = 48 oz.
        1/2 lb. = 8 oz.

    e. 1 hr. = 60 min.
        3 hr. = 180 min.
        1/2 hr. = 30 min.

    f. 1 min. = 60 sec.
        3 min. = 180 sec.
        1/2 min. = 30 sec.

    g. 1 ton = 2,000 pounds
        3 tons = 6,000 pounds
        1/2 ton = 1,000 pounds

    h. 1 acre = 43,560 sq. ft.
        3 acres = 130,680 sq. ft.
        1/2 acre = 21,780 sq. ft.

    i. 1 ft. = 12 in.
        3 ft. = 36 in.
        1/2 ft. = 6 in.

Extension: The Foreman's Problem

1. The co-workers' measurements are accurate. Explanations will vary. Sample explanation: The length of the foundation is 15 feet, which is the same as 5 yd., or 12 ft. and 1 yd. The width of the building is 9 feet, which is the same as 36 in. (3 ft.) and 72 in. (6 ft.).

2. 48 feet or 16 yards or 576 inches

3. $43.20

Test Practice

1. (4)

2. (4)

3. (3)

4. (4)

5. (3)

6. 192

Lesson 9: Squarely in English

Activity: Squarely in English

Group 1:

How many square inches are in a square foot? <u>144</u>

Group 2:

How many square feet are in a square yard? <u>9</u>

Group 3:

How many square inches are in a square yard? <u>1,296</u>

Practice: Choose a Unit

Suggested answers:

<u>d, e</u>	the length of the window frame
<u>a</u>	the surface space of a window sill
<u>a</u>	the space the stamp takes up on an envelope
<u>e, f</u>	the length of two tables pushed together
<u>a, b</u>	metal to construct a street sign
<u>a, b</u>	floor space of a child's playpen
<u>a</u>	size of a calendar page
<u>b, c</u>	tiles to cover a hotel lobby floor
<u>e, f</u>	height of a swing
<u>e, f</u>	length of a pool
<u>e, f</u>	distance to the nearest bathroom
<u>b, c</u>	victory banner covering an entire wall of a school
<u>d, e</u>	depth of a bookshelf
<u>a</u>	aluminum foil to cover a baking pan

Practice: Roll Out the Carpet

1. The price of the carpet is the same whether it is purchased by the square foot or the square yard. There are 9 square feet in 1 square yard: $2.78 × 9 = $25.02.

2. 144 square inches = 1 square foot

3. **a.** $50.04
   b. Answers will vary.

4. 3,097,600 square yards = 1 square mile. A square mile = 1 mile × 1 mile, which is the same as 1,760 yd. × 1,760 yd.

5. A total of 21,120 sq. ft. of carpeting would cost $58,713.60.

Practice: The Better Deal

1. Plywood: $0.45 × 9 sq. ft = $4.05

   Space-blanket material: 3 ft. = 1 yd. = $4.50.

   The plywood would be more cost effective because it would be cheaper (and there would be no waste).

2. There would be 27 sq. ft. of glass left over. A 2 yd. by 2 yd. piece of glass = 6 ft. by 6 ft. = 36 sq. ft. of glass. The 3 × 3 window = 9 sq. ft. 36 − 9 = 27.

3. Answers may vary, depending on how the strapping is used. A sample answer: 156 inches of strapping, or 13 feet.

Practice: San Diego Construction Company

The San Diego Company started constructing a fence around a park. They marked the boundaries of the park with 210 feet of tape. Before ordering the fencing at $6.75 per foot, two workers checked the measurements. Because the park was shaped like a <u>rectangle</u>, they only needed to measure the <u>length (or width)</u> and the <u>width (or length)</u>. The length was <u>75</u> feet. The 210-foot figure was correct. The width measured <u>30</u>. At $6.75 per foot, the fencing would cost about <u>$1,400</u> .

The plan called for a tiled walkway straight across the center of the park, parallel to the length. The walkway's dimensions were 75 feet long and 4 feet wide. The company planned to lay <u>300</u> one-sq.-ft. cement tiles. At $2.59 per tile, the estimated cost was $780.

Practice: Area Measurements

1. Answers will vary. Sample answer based on measuring a book 6 inches by 9 inches.

   a. Book

   b. 6 inches by 9 inches

c.

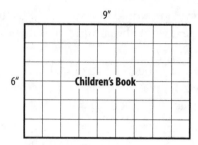

d. *A* = 54 sq. in.

2. 1   18 in. **x** 3 ft.
   4.5 sq. ft. (or 648 sq. in.)
   Answers will vary. Sample answer: Change
   18 in. to 1.5 feet (12 in. = 1 ft., 6 in. = 1/2
   ft.), then multiply 1.5 by 3.

   2   3 ft. **x** 6 ft.
   18 sq. ft. (or 2 sq. yd.)

   3   6 ft. **x** 3 yd.
   54 sq. ft. (or 6 sq. yd.)

3. Answers will vary. Sample composite shape:

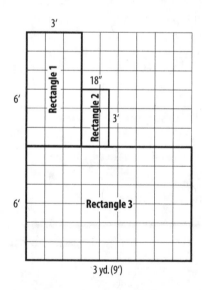

4. Answers will vary. Sample answer based on
composite shape above:

Area of composite shape: 76.5 sq. ft. (or 9.5 sq.
   yd.)

Perimeter of composite shape: 42 ft.

Extension: Checkerboard Paint Job

1. Area of each square within the checkerboard:
   81 sq. in.

2. Area of Sue's giant checkerboard: 36 sq. ft.

Test Practice

1. (4)

2. (2)

3. (4)

4. (2)

5. (3)

6. 2,592 sq. in.

Lesson 10: Scale Down

Activity 1: Sketch the Door

Sketches will vary.

Activity 2: Mathematician Uses Scale

Sketches will vary. Sample scaling of a door:

1. Answers should be similar to the following:

Steps to make a scale drawing:

   1. Figure out the number of squares on the
      grid paper.

   2. Figure out the measurement of the object
      to be scaled.

   3. Figure out what one grid will equal—a
      whole inch, cm, foot—or at least a
      benchmark whole number like 10 inches or
      cm.

2. Answers will vary.

4″
4″ ☐ ⟶ Each grid = 16 square inches

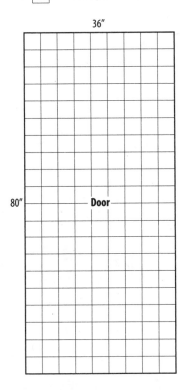

Practice: Scale Drawings

1. Answers will vary. Example of scale of book:

1′
1′ ☐ ⟶ Each grid = 1 square foot

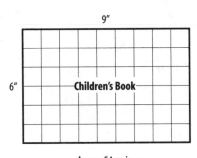

Area = 8 sq. ft.

2. Answers will vary. Sample scale of a table top:

1″
1″ ☐ ⟶ Each grid = 1 square inch

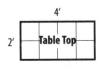

Area = 54 sq. in.

Practice: Shrinking Doors

1. Answers will vary. Sample answer:

  a. <u>1 cm</u> = 1 foot

  b. length = <u>7 cm</u>   width = <u>4 cm</u>

  c. length = <u>1 cm</u>   width = <u>1 cm</u>

2. Answers will vary. Sample answer:

  a. <u>2 cm</u> = 1 foot

  b. length = <u>12 cm</u>   width = <u>6 cm</u>

  c. length = <u>4 cm</u>   width = <u>2 cm</u>

3. Answers will vary. Sample answer:

  a. <u>2 cm</u> = 1 foot

  b. length = <u>12 cm</u>   width = <u>10 cm</u>

  c. length = <u>3 cm</u>   width = <u>4 cm</u>

4. Answers will vary. Sample answer:

  a. length = <u>.17 cm</u> width = <u>1 cm</u>

  b. length = <u>7 cm</u>   width = <u>4 cm</u>

Practice: All About Shapes

1. A similar shape that is half the size of Shape 1 will have angles that measure <u>150°</u> and sides that measure <u>1</u> cm.

2. True

3. False

4. True

5. False

6.

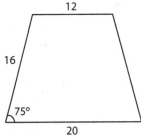

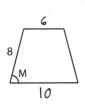

7. ∠M = 75°

8. a. Answers will vary. Sample answer:

$\frac{1}{2}$ mi.
$\frac{1}{2}$ mi. ☐

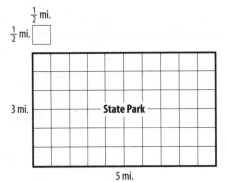

b. Answers will vary. Answer based on scale above: 1 cm = 1/2 mile

c. Answers will vary. Answer based on scale above: 60 sq. cm

d. 15 sq. miles

Extension: Enlarge It

Answers will vary. Sample answers below based on card 12 cm by 16 cm.

1. Length = <u>12 cm</u>   width = <u>16 cm</u>
2. Length = <u>18 cm</u>   width = <u>24 cm</u>
3. 1 cm = 2/3 cm (or 3 cm = 2 cm) because the new shape is 1.5 times larger than the original
4. Length = <u>9 cm</u>   width = <u>12 cm</u>
5. 1 cm = one 1/3 cm (or 3 cm = 4 cm) because the new shape is 3/4 of the original

Test Practice

1. (5)
2. (4)
3. (4)
4. (2)
5. (2)
6. 225

Interim Assessment 2: A Fresh Look

Activity 1: Fixing Up the Classroom

Plans will vary, depending on whether students pick the walls, floor, or ceiling.

All plans will require measuring length and width. The more efficient tools to use will be meter sticks, yardsticks, or measuring tapes. If students are measuring with a ruler, it will take longer and probably not be as accurate a reading.

The molding measurements will be in linear units; the floor and wall measurements will be in square units.

Activity 2: Home, Sweet Home

Task 1

1. Line A is about 1 inch long (or about 2.5 cm).
2. Line B is about 6 inches long (or about 15 cm).
3. Answers will vary. Two suggested ways to find the perimeter of a rectangular table: (1) Measure the sides of the table, then add all four sides together.

(2) Measure the length and width of the table. Add the length and the width, then multiply the total by two.

4. 576 sq. in.
5. 9 square foot tiles

Task 2

6. 16 feet
7. 192 inches
8. Answers will vary, depending on the size of the classroom door. Sample answer based on a door that measures 36″ by 78″:

   Maria's bathroom door is 1 foot narrower and 6 inches shorter.

   or

   Maria's bathroom door has 7.5 sq. ft. less area.

9. The comparison is based on a classroom door having a width of 3 feet and a height of 80 inches.

Task 3

10. To carpet the master suite will require <u>144</u> sq. ft. of carpet, or <u>16</u> sq. yd.
11. There are 144 sq. ft. (12 x 12) of floor space in the master suite and 100 sq. ft (10 x 10) in the other bedroom. The master suite has 44 sq. ft more floor space.
12. **a.** 320 sq. ft. will be added to the living space.
    b. 1,440 sq. ft. total living space
13. $20.85 ($6.95 x 3)

Test Practice

14. (3)
15. (2)

Lesson 11: Filling the Room

Activity: Filling the Room

See *Activity* description in *Teacher's Book* for suggestions on what to observe as students work through this activity.

Practice: How Many Fit?

If Kat uses 9″ across the width of the shelf, and 12″ deep, she can fit 6 containers in two layers for a total of 12. If she uses 4″ across and 12″ deep, she can fit 8 containers and only one layer.

Practice: Measuring Things

Answers will vary. Sample answers below:

a. Phone book
$l = \underline{27\ cm}$ $w = \underline{21\ cm}$ $h = \underline{4\ cm}$

b. Jewelry box
$l = \underline{25\ cm}$ $w = \underline{24\ cm}$ $h = \underline{5\ cm}$

c. Ice cube tray
$l = \underline{28\ cm}$ $w = \underline{12\ cm}$ $h = \underline{3\ cm}$

d. VCR
$l = \underline{44\ cm}$ $w = \underline{48\ cm}$ $h = \underline{8\ cm}$

e. A door
$l = \underline{203\ cm}$ $w = \underline{91\ cm}$ $h = \underline{4\ cm}$

2. Answers will vary.

3. Answers will vary.

Practice: Area, Perimeter, or Volume?

1. **a.** Perimeter
   b. You measure the length and width of the playground to figure the distance around it.

2. **a.** Volume
   b. You measure how much dirt a truck will hold by figuring out how wide, long, and high the pile in the truck can be.

3. **a.** Area
   b. You measure the length of the hallway and the height of the wall to figure out the amount of paint you will need for the space.

4. **a.** Volume
   b. You measure the depth of the pool as well as its length and width (or its circumference and radius if it is circular).

5. **a.** Area
   b. You measure how high and how long the walls of the shed are.

Extension: Pack It In

Answers will vary. Sample answers below based on a refrigerator shelf size of 26 inches wide, 18 inches deep, and 7 inches high:

1. The refrigerator shelf is 26 inches wide, 18 inches deep, and 7 inches high.

2. The egg carton to be stored in the refrigerator is about 5 inches wide, 12 inches long, and 3 1/4 inches high (which will be rounded to 4 inches so that the eggs will not be crushed).

3. If the eggs are stored widthwise on the refrigerator shelf, 5 cartons will fit because the cartons cannot be more than one row deep. (If I risked crushing the eggs, I could store another row on top because the actual height is 3 1/4 inches. Two stacks of cartons would be about 6 1/2 inches high. By packing the cartons in this way, 10 cartons of eggs would fit on the shelf.)

   If the eggs are stored lengthwise on the refrigerator shelf, 6 cartons will fit, two per row and 3 rows deep. (If I risked crushing the eggs, I could store another row on top because the actual height is 3 1/4 inches. Two stacks of cartons would be about 6 1/2 inches high. With this method of packing, 12 cartons of eggs would fit on the shelf.)

4. Answers will vary.

Test Practice

1. (4)
2. (3)
3. (2)
4. (5)
5. (3)
6. 12

Lesson 12: Cheese Cubes, Anyone?

Activity 1: Inside the Wrapper

Wrapper 1: 15 cu. in.

Wrapper 2: 12 cu. in.

Wrapper 3: 12 cu. in.

Activity 2: Cheese for a Party

Strategies for finding the answers will vary. A sample strategy is explained below:

1. **Cheese, Anyone?**

   A 3″ by 3″ by 4″ block yields 36 1″ cubes of cheese. If each person is to have 9 cubes of cheese, you need 180 pieces (9 x 20 = 180). Five blocks of cheese will give you 180 cubes (5 x 36 = 180).

2. **Volume Savings?**

   A 15″ by 15″ by 20″ yields 4,500 1″ cubes of cheese. That's a lot of cheese! Much more than is needed. CJ multiplied all three dimensions by

5, but he only needed to multiply one of the dimensions by 5.

Instead of buying five 3″ by 3″ by 4″ blocks, you could buy either a block that is 3″ by 3″ by 20″ *or* 3″ by 15″ by 4″ *or* 15″ by 3″ by 4″.

Practice: Pack That Ice Cream

If Odie packs the blocks of ice cream flat, she could pack 8 on a shelf, and 16 on the two shelves. She can pack them 4 across a row (6 x 4 = 24″ wide) with 2 rows (6 x 2 = 12″ deep), but she can only pack them 1 row high because the ice cream is 4″ tall and the shelf is 6″ high.

If Odie packs the blocks of ice cream on their sides, she could pack 12 on a shelf, and 24 on the two shelves. She can pack them 6 across a row (4 x 6 = 24″ wide) with 2 rows (6 x 2 = 12″ deep), but she can only pack them 1 row high because the ice cream, on its side, is 6″ tall and so is the shelf.

Practice: Comparing Volumes

Box A has a volume of 32 cubic cm. It is 4 cm long, 4 cm wide, and 2 cm high.

Box B has a volume of 36 cubic cm. It is 6 cm long, 3 cm wide, and 2 cm high.

Practice: Missing Dimensions

1. Missing dimension: 3 cm
2. Missing dimension: 4 in.
3. Missing dimension: 9 cm
4. Missing dimension: 5 in.

Extension: A Special Box

The volume of the box is 180 cu. in.

Test Practice

1. (4)
2. (1)
3. (4)
4. (3)
5. (5)
6. 10

Lesson 13: On the Surface

Activity 1: Surface Area of a Box

1. **How much cardboard or paper on the cheese-wrapper?**

Wrapper 1:
Length: $l = 5$ in. Width: $w = 3$ in.

Height: $h = 1$ in. Volume: $V = 15$ cu. in.
Surface Area: $S = 46$ sq. in.

Wrapper 2:
Length: $l = 3$ in. Width: $w = 2$ in.
Height: $h = 2$ in. Volume: $V = 12$ cu. in.
Surface Area: $S = 32$ sq. in.

Wrapper 3:
Length: $l = 4$ in. Width: $w = 3$ in.
Height: $h = 1$ in. Volume: $V = 12$ cu. in.
Surface Area: $S = 38$ sq. in.

2. **How much cardboard or paper on the box?**
Length: $l = 6$ in. Width: $w = 3$ in.
Height: $h = 1$ in. Volume: $V = 18$ cu. in.
Surface Area: $S = 54$ sq. in.

Activity 2: Cardboard Needed

Box A:
Length: $l = 6$ cm Width: $w = 3$ cm
Height: $h = 2$ cm Volume: $V = 36$ cu. cm
Surface Area: $S = 72$ sq. cm

Box B:
Length: $l = 4$ cm Width: $w = 3$ cm
Height: $h = 3$ cm Volume: $V = 36$ cu. cm
Surface Area: $S = 66$ sq. cm

Box C:
Length: $l = 9$ cm Width: $w = 2$ cm
Height: $h = 2$ cm Volume: $V = 36$ cu. cm
Surface Area: $S = 80$ sq. cm

Box D:
Length: $l = 9$ cm Width: $w = 4$ cm
Height: $h = 1$ cm Volume: $V = 36$ cu. cm
Surface Area: $S = 98$ sq. cm

1. The volume of each of the boxes is the same: 36 cu. cm.

2. Answers will vary. Sample answer: The longer the box, the greater the surface area.

3. The box requiring the most cardboard to make is the one with the largest surface area: 9 cm by 4 cm by 1 cm.

Practice: Surface Area vs. Volume

1. Box A: 180 cu. cm
   Box B: 180 cu. cm

2. Box B is cheaper to make because it has less surface area (216 sq. cm). Box A has a surface area of 222 cu. cm.

Practice: Small Box Volumes

1. Predictions will vary.

2. A   6 cm   4 cm   2 cm   48 cu. cm

   B   12 cm   2 cm   2 cm   48 cu. cm

   C   4 cm   4 cm   3 cm   48 cu. cm

   D   6 cm   2 cm   2 cm   24 cu. cm

   E   3 cm   2 cm   2 cm   12 cu. cm

3. Boxes A, B, and C have the same volume.

4. Answers will vary.

5. Answers will vary. One possible response: the volume takes all three dimensions into account so, although a 6 cm by 2 cm by 1 cm box has a volume of 12 cu. cm (6 x 2 x 1 = 12), that same volume can come from a 12 cm by 1 cm by 1 cm box (12 x 1 x 1 = 12).

6. Answers will vary. For example, a 31 cm x 4 cm x 3 cm box would hold them all: 6 cm + 12 cm + 4 cm + 6 cm + 3 cm = 31 cm for the length; the width is 4 cm, and the height is 3 cm. The volume of this box is 372 sq. cm.

Practice: Vocabulary Review

Answers will vary but should use students' words rather than a dictionary definition.

Extension: Concrete Solutions

1. 27 cu. feet = 1 cu. yd.

2. 81 cu. ft. = 3 cu. yd.

3. 4 cu. yd. = 108 cu. ft.

4.

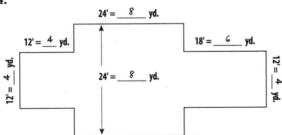

104 cu. yd. needed for the foundation
[(4 x 4 x 1) + (8 x 8 x 1) + (6 x 4 x 1)]

Test Practice

1. (5)

2. (1)

3. (2)

4. (2)

5. (1)

6. 24

Closing the Unit: Design a Box

Final Assessment

Task 1: Shape Names, Angles, Perimeter

1. a. Shape name: <u>square</u>

   b. Measure of all angles: <u>90°</u>

   c. Actual length of each side: <u>20 ft.</u>

   d. Amount of wood needed: <u>80 ft</u>

2. a. Shape name: <u>(equilateral) triangle</u>

   b. Measure of all angles: <u>60°</u>

   c. Actual length of each side: <u>20 ft</u>

   d. Amount of wood needed: <u>60 ft</u>

3. a. Shape name: <u>hexagon</u>

   b. Measure of all angles: <u>120°</u>

   c. Actual length of each side: <u>20 ft</u>

   d. Amount of wood needed: <u>120 ft</u>

Task 2: Area and Perimeter

1. a. Perimeter = <u>504</u> inches

   b. Perimeter = <u>42</u> in feet

   c. Perimeter = <u>14</u> in yards

2. <u>74</u> square-foot tiles

Task 3: Volume

Answers will vary, depending on the size of the box the teacher uses.

Task 4: Area to Scale

2.

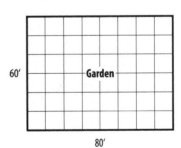

3. Answers will vary. Sample scale: 1 cm = 10 feet

4. Answers will vary. Sample ways to divide the garden:

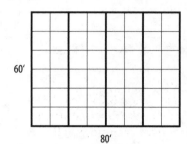

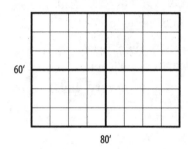

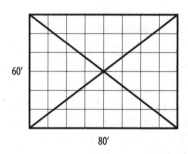

5. Each friend's plot is 1,200 sq. ft.

Task 5: Test Type

1. (1)
2. (2)
3. (2)
4. (2)
5. (4)
6. (4)

Sources and Resources

Mathematics Education

The National Council of Teachers of Mathematics (NCTM) publishes several excellent resources.

- *Principles and Standards for School Mathematics.* Reston, VA: NCTM, 2000.
- The NCTM journals: *Mathematics Teaching in the Middle Grades, Mathematics Teacher,* and *Journal for Research in Mathematics Education.*
- http://www.nctm.org

Fendel, D., D. Resek, L. Alper, & S. Fraser. *Interactive Mathematics Program.* Berkeley, CA: Key Curriculum Press, 1997.

Lappan, G., J. Fey, W. Fitzgerald, S. Friel, & E. Phillips. *Connected Mathematics Series.* Parsippany, NJ: Dale Seymour Publications, Division of Pearson Education, 1998.

National Research Council. *Adding It Up: Helping Children Learn Mathematics.* J. Kilpatrick, J. Swafford, and B. Findell (Eds.). Mathematics Learning Study Committee, Center for Education, Division of Behavioral and Social Sciences and Education. Washington, DC: National Academy Press, 2001.

Russell, S.J., et al. *The Investigations in Number, Data, and Space Curriculum.* White Plains, NY: Dale Seymour Publications, 1998.

Mathematics and Numeracy Education for Adults

Curry, D., M.J. Schmitt, and S. Waldron. *A Framework for Adult Numeracy Standards: The Mathematical Skills and Abilities Adults Need to Be Equipped for the Future.* Boston: World Education, 1996. (This framework was developed by members of the Adult Numeracy Network.) http://shell04.theworld.com/std/anpn

Massachusetts Department of Education. *Massachusetts Adult Basic Education Curriculum Frameworks for Mathematics and Numeracy.* Malden, MA: Massachusetts Department of Education, 2001. http://www.doe.mass.edu/acls/frameworks

Stein, S. *Equipped for the Future Content Standards: What Adults Need to Know and Be Able to Do in the Twenty-First Century.* ED Pubs document EX0099P. Washington, DC: National Institute for Literacy, 2000.

Geometry and Measurement

Clements, Douglas, and George Bright (eds.). 2003 NCTM Yearbook, *Learning and Teaching Measurement.* Reston, VA: National Council of Teachers of Mathematics, 2003.

Crowley, Mary L. "The van Heile Model of the Development of Geometric Thought." 1987 NCTM Yearbook, *Learning and Teaching Measurement.* Reston, VA: National Council of Teachers of Mathematics, 1987.

Gutiérrez, A., A. Jaime, and J.M. Fortuny. "An Alternative Paradigm to Evaluate the Acquisition of the van Hiele Levels." *Journal for Research in Mathematics Education,* 22 (1991).

Malloy, Carol E., and Susan Friel. "Perimeter and Area through the van Heile Model." *Mathematics Teaching in the Middle School,* 5, no. 2 (October, 1999).

Pappas, Theoni, "Triangles," in *Math Talk: Mathematical Ideas in Poems for Two Voices.* Wide World Publishing, 1991.

Robichaux, Rebecca R., and Paulette R. Rodrigue. "Using Origami to Promote Geometric Communication." *Mathematics Teaching in the Middle School,* 9, no. 4 (December, 2003).

Web Sites

The web can add color and movement to the lessons you do from the EMPower unit, *Over, Around, and Within: Geometry and Measurement.*

For moveable pattern block shapes on line, see http://arcytech.org/java/patterns/patterns_j.shtml

For pattern blocks, see http://www.best.com/~ejad/java/patterns

For answers to geometry-related questions, see http://mathforum.org/dr.math/

For a geometry reference resource for children and adults, see http://w3.byuh.edu/library/curriculum/Geometry/Geometry.htm

For checking estimates for *A Fresh Look* with Home Depot's online calculator, see http://www.homedepot.com

For information on fractal geometry, see
http://www.strengthinperspective.com/MPART/MPGAL5/mpgal5.html

Geometry and Art Web Sites

http://www.imart.org/education/IMA_education/volume.asp?levelid=2

http://www.isibrno.cz/~gott/mandalas.htm

http://www.ed.uri.edu/SMART96/ELEMATH/GeometryArt/geometry.html

http://www.myschoolonline.com/content_gallery/0,3138,52947-130799-56-6394,00.html

http://www.cs.berkeley.edu/~sequin/SCULPTS/

http://mathforum.org/~sarah/shapiro/

http://www.cs.berkeley.edu/~sequin/ART/

http://www.lotuslazuli.com/contents.htm

http://www.mathcs.carleton.edu/penrose/index.html